How To Salad

Disclaimer
This manual is not intended to provide medical advice or to take the place of medical advice and treatment from your personal physician. Readers are advised to consult their own doctors or other qualified health professionals regarding the treatment of medical conditions. The author shall not be held liable or responsible for any misunderstanding or misuse of the information contained in this manual or for any loss, damage, or injury caused or alleged to be caused directly or indirectly by any treatment, action, or application of any food or food source discussed in this manual. The statements in this book have not been evaluated by the U.S. Food and Drug Administration. This information is not intended to diagnose, treat, cure, or prevent any disease.
To request permission for reproduction or inquire about private nutritional consulting or speaking engagements, contact:

Isabel De Los Rios
Live Smart Solutions Inc.
2345 7th Street
Denver, CO 80211
E-mail: questions@beyonddiet.com

Contents

Introduction

This guide includes some fantastic salad recipes, submitted by our very own Beyond Diet customers. All recipes have been thoroughly reviewed and approved by me to ensure that each one follows all Beyond Diet requirements.

Because Beyond Diet does promote the inclusion of many fruits and vegetables into your daily meal plans, it is essential to keep your salads new, fun and interesting. Eating the same foods, especially salad, again and again leads to boredom and abandonment. To prevent this from happening, I highly encourage you to try at least one new recipe per week that suits your meal plan. Also, be adventurous and try some foods that you have never tried before.

Also, remember that allowable food servings and portion sizes differ for each person, depending on metabolic type and the number of calories required daily. Please adjust recipe portions to suit your meal plan, as instructed in the Chapter on Daily Meal Planning, according to the Allowable Servings Guide and the Food Choices charts. For example, if you are a Carb Type allowed four 1-oz servings of protein for dinner and a salad recipe calls for 6 oz of chicken (or doesn't specify a portion size), eat only 4 oz of chicken with your meal.

Remember, fresh food is best, and the more whole and natural the food you eat, the healthier you will be—and the better you will feel. Enjoy your yummy salad!

With all of the recipes presented here (and with any other recipe you may choose to use), adhere to all the principles taught in the manual. Here are a few points to remember and consider for each recipe:

Go Organic	Organic ingredients are always best.
Meats, Poultry, Eggs, & Fish	Whenever possible, choose free-range, hormone- and antibiotic-free, fresh, and wild meats, poultry, eggs, and fish.
Salt	Use an unrefined sea salt or, preferably, Celtic sea salt or Redmond's Real Salt. http://go.beyonddiet.com/SBGetCelticSeaSalt
Oils	The best oils to use for cooking are coconut oil, butter or ghee. http://go.beyonddiet.com/SBGetCoconutOil
Water	Water should be pure and filtered. http://go.beyonddiet.com/SBGetWaterFiltration
Honey	Honey should always be raw. http://go.beyonddiet.com/SBGetRawHoney
Sweeteners	Stevia or Xylitol can be used instead of raw honey. http://go.beyonddiet.com/SBGetStevia
General Ingredients	Fresh ingredients with minimal processing are always best.
Cheese	Cheese should be raw and organic.
Yogurt	Yogurt should be full fat and organic.
Butter	Organic butter from grass fed cows is your best choice. http://go.beyonddiet.com/SBGetRawButter

Mediterranean Salads

Greek Shrimp Salad

Servings: 4
Proteins/Carbs/Fats: 3 / 2 / 3

Ingredients

1 lb Raw Shrimp (peeled)

To Taste Sea Salt and Pepper

2 Medium Tomatoes (chopped)

1 Cucumber (chopped)

1/2 cup Crumbled Feta Cheese (may substitute fresh shaved parmesan)

1/2-1 cup Pitted Kalamata or other Black Olives

1/4 cup Olive Oil

4 tsp Red Wine Vinegar

1 (10 oz) bag (or more) Baby Spinach Leaves, Spring Mix or Romaine Lettuce

Directions

Cook shrimp by grilling or boiling.

If grilling, thread shrimp onto metal skewers or bamboo ones that have been soaked in water for 15 minutes. Brush both sides with oil and season with sea salt and pepper. Grill shrimp until fully cooked, about 2 minutes per side.

Meanwhile, mix in a medium bowl the tomatoes, cucumbers, cheese, olives, oregano, 2 tablespoons of the olive oil and 2 teaspoons of the vinegar. Add shrimp to bowl. Lightly toss ingredients to coat. Set aside. (Can be made an hour or so ahead.)

When ready to serve, drizzle remaining oil, 2 teaspoons of vinegar, as well as a generous sprinkling of sea salt and pepper, over spinach or lettuce in a large bowl. Toss to coat. Divide greens among 4 large plates. Top with a portion of the shrimp mixture.

Submitted By: Dianne L. - Clinton Township, Michigan

Mediterranean Barley Rice Salad

Servings: 6
Proteins/Carbs/Fats: 0 / 3 / 1

Ingredients

1 cup (250 mL) Pearl Barley (rinsed)

1 cup (250 mL) Basamati Rice (rinsed)

3 cups (750 mL) Cherry Tomatoes

1/2 Large Red Onion

1 Sweet Red Pepper

1 English Cucumber

4 cups (1 L) Baby Spinach (coarsely chopped)

1 pkg (200g) Feta Cheese (crumbled)

Directions

In saucepan of boiling salted water, cook barley until tender, about 20 minutes. Drain and rinse under cold water, drain well. Let stand for 10 minutes to dry. Transfer to large bowl.

Meanwhile, in separate saucepan, bring 1 1/2 cups (375ml) salted water to boil. Add rice, cover, reduce heat and simmer until tender and no liquid remains, about 15 minutes. Let stand for 5 minutes. Add to barley mixture, let cool.

Cut tomatoes in half, add to barley mixture. Cut onion, red pepper and cucumber into 1-inch (2.5cm) chunks, add to barley, tossing to combine.

Pour dressing over salad and toss to coat. Refrigerate for 30 minutes, or up to 24 hours.

Submitted By: Tammy K. – Calgary, Alberta, Canada

Tabouli – The Queen of Lebanese Salads

Servings: 4
Proteins/Carbs/Fats: 0 / 1 / 1

Ingredients

3 Large Bunches of Parsley

1/3 cup Bulgur

2 cups Boiling Water

4 Green Onions with Green Tops (diced small)

1/4 cup Fresh Mint (finely chopped, or 2 Tbsp dry)

2 Large Tomatoes (diced small)

1/2 tsp Sea Salt

1/4 tsp Freshly Ground Pepper

1/3 cup Lemon Juice (or to taste)

1/4 cup Extra Virgin Olive Oil

To Serve Romaine Lettuce Leaves

Directions

Wash the parsley well, drain, and shake out excess moisture.

Soak bulgur in boiling water in a large bowl for 2 minutes. Drain well. Set aside to cool while preparing other ingredients.

Remove stems from parsley and discard. Chop parsley very fine (3 bunches should yield about 5 cups). Add to bulgur.

Add onions, mint, tomatoes, salt, pepper, lemon juice and oil. (If not serving immediately, do not add tomatoes and onions until just before serving.) Toss well.

Serve with Romaine lettuce leaves. Tear leaves into bite-sized pieces and use to scoop up salad for eating.

Submitted By: Penny – Ottawa, Ontario, Canada

Moroccan Carrot Salad

Ingredients

Carrots

Green or Dark Reddish Olives

Fresh Parsley

Olive Oil

Cumin

Lemon Juice

Salt

Fresh Garlic

Directions

Adjust amount of each ingredient to taste.

Cut carrots into round pieces.

Boil carrots with some salt; then drain them.

Add olives, olive oil, parsley, a bit of cumin, lemon juice and rasped fresh garlic to the carrots. Mix; heat mixture for awhile while stirring.

Let the carrots cool.

Serve immediately, or refrigerate for a few hours before serving.

Submitted By: Nezha H.

Bulgur Salad

Servings: 6
Proteins/Carbs/Fats: 0 / 1 / .5

Ingredients

1 cup Fresh-Squeezed Orange Juice

1 cup Bulgur

1/2 cup Dried Cranberries (chopped)

1/2 cup Celery (diced)

1/2 cup English Cucumber (peeled and diced)

1/4 cup Red Onion (minced)

1/4 cup Walnuts (chopped)

1/3 cup Fresh Parsley (chopped)

2 Tbsp Fresh Mint Leaves (chopped)

1 Tbsp Olive Oil

1 Tbsp Freshly Squeezed Lemon Juice

1 tsp Grated Lemon Zest

1/4 tsp Salt

1/8 tsp Freshly Ground Black Pepper

Directions

Combine orange juice and 1 cup water in a medium saucepan.

Bring to a boil over high heat. Reduce to low and stir in bulgur. Simmer, covered, until bulgur has absorbed all of the liquid (15 to 20 minutes).

Meanwhile, place cranberries, celery, cucumber, red onions and nuts in a large bowl.

Add cooked bulgur, parsley, mint, olive oil, lemon juice, lemon zest, salt, and pepper.

Mix well. Cover and refrigerate at least 2 hours before serving.

Submitted By: Betty C.

Mediterranean Grilled Chopped Vegetable Salad

Servings: 8
Proteins/Carbs/Fats: 0 / 2 / 3

Ingredients

1 Medium Eggplant

1 Medium Zucchini

1 Medium Yellow Squash

1 Medium Fennel Bulb

1 Small Red Onion

8 Asparagus Spears

3/4 cup Extra-Virgin Olive Oil

To Taste Sea Salt

To Taste Freshly Ground Black Pepper

Water

30 Green Beans (trimmed)

10 Baby Carrots (trimmed)

1/2 cup Kalamata Olives (pitted and halved)

1 cup Mixed Baby Lettuces

1/2 cup Crumbled Raw Feta Cheese, Plus 1/4 Pound Block (optional)

3 Tbsp Lemon Juice

3 Tbsp Sherry Vinegar

1/2 cup Sun-Dried Tomato Vinaigrette (see Dressings)

1/4 cup Parsley (fresh chopped)

Directions

Cut the eggplant, zucchini and squash diagonally into slices 1/2 inch thick. Trim the fennel and cut crosswise into slices 1/2 inch thick. Peel the onion and cut crosswise into slices 1/2 inch thick. Trim the asparagus.

With 1/2 cup of the olive oil, coat all the vegetables. Season with salt and pepper. Set the vegetables aside.

Build a fire in a charcoal grill, or preheat a gas grill, for indirect-heat cooking.

Meanwhile, bring a large pot of salted water to a boil and fill a mixing bowl with ice and water. Add the green beans to the boiling water and, as soon as it returns to the boil and the beans are bright green, use a wire skimmer or slotted spoon to transfer them to the ice water. Add the baby carrots and boil until tender-crisp, 2-3 minutes; transfer to the ice water. Drain the vegetables and set aside.

When the fire is hot, place the vegetables on the cooking grid not directly above the heat. Cook, turning as necessary to prevent scorching, until are nicely browned and tender-crisp, 5-7 minutes total cooking time. As they are done, transfer the vegetables to a platter and leave to cool.

Cut the grilled vegetables into 1/2-inch pieces. Cut the carrots and green beans on the bias into 1/4-inch pieces.

Submitted By: Angela M. - Kennedy Saskatchewan Canada

Creamy Salads

Potato Salad with Red Radishes, Green Onions and Champignon Mushrooms

Ingredients

Potatoes

Equal parts Red Radishes and Mushrooms

Green Onions

Lettuce (the crunchier sort, the better)

Plain Yogurt or Kefir with Live Cultures

Isabel's Homemade Mayonnaise (see Dressings section)

Salt and Pepper

*For this salad, there is no set quantity of ingredients. You can use more or less of each ingredient, depending on your mood, taste, or what is available. However, potato is the main ingredient so it should dominate while the rest are just complementing and flavoring the salad.

Directions

Boil potatoes with their peel on until they are done (so you can easily slide a fork in them). Take them out of the water and let them cool. When they are cool enough to touch, peel them and roughly chop them into 1-inch cubes. If you're using baby potatoes, no need to peel them, just chop them into halves or quarters.

Chop radishes and mushrooms in slices and add them in with the potatoes. Make sure the potatoes have cooled completely by the time you start adding in the rest of the ingredients.

Chop the green onions including the green part and add them to the mix.

Add equal parts mayo and yogurt, salt and pepper to taste and toss everything together until mixed.

It can be served immediately or refrigerated for later use or even the next day. Good on its own, also great with meats done on the barbecue.

For a lighter version on hot summer days, it can be done with yogurt or kefir only, without the mayonnaise. Just double the quantity of the yogurt or kefir.

Submitted By: Sorana - Canada

Egg Salad

Servings: 6
Proteins/Carbs/Fats: 2 / 0 / 0

Ingredients

5 Organic Hard-Boiled Eggs
2 cups Cottage Cheese
1 Tbsp Finely Diced Onion
1/2 cup Plain Greek Yogurt
3 dashes Sea Salt
2 Tbsp Mustard

Directions

Finely chop the hard-boiled eggs.

Mix in the rest of the ingredients.

Add more salt and mustard as needed.

Enjoy!

Pok-a-Dot Coleslaw

Servings: 4
Proteins/Carbs/Fats: 0 / 1 / 1

Ingredients

1 Large Head of Cabbage

1 Large Sweet Red Pepper

1 Tbsp Whole Caraway Seed

8 oz can Crushed Pineapple in Pineapple Juice

1/4 cup Isabel's Homemade Mayonnaise (see Dressings section)

1/4 cup Plain Yogurt

Directions

Cut cabbage in half and shred only one half. Put other half back in refrigerator.

Chop the sweet red pepper into ½ -inch pieces.

Drain the crushed pineapple and save the juice, some to be used in dressing.

In a bowl, toss the shredded cabbage, chopped red pepper, and drained crushed pineapple. Add the caraway seed.

Blend mayonnaise, yogurt, and one tablespoon of the pineapple juice. Add to the cabbage mixture, and mix well.

Cover and refrigerate for at least 30 minutes.

Makes 4-6 servings.

Submitted By: Victoria – Fairbanks, Alaska

Creamy Cucumber Salad

Servings: 1
Proteins/Carbs/Fats: 0 / 2 / 0

Ingredients

1 Cucumber (peeled and thinly sliced)

1/2 cup Plain Yogurt

3 Tbsp Red Wine Vinegar

To Taste Stevia (optional)

To Taste Sea Salt and Freshly Ground Pepper

Directions

Stir together yogurt and vinegar in a medium bowl adjusting amounts to desired thickness and taste. Add sliced cucumber, stirring to coat. If too tangy, add a little Stevia to balance flavor. Season with salt and pepper. Chill before serving if there's time.

This basic recipe can be changed up to use what's in the house: plain or Greek yogurt; flavored vinegars; throw in thinly sliced red onion, celery, fennel, red or green pepper; add herbs such as basil or mint, fresh or dried.

Submitted By: Sarah S. – Phoenix, Arizona

Waldorf Salad

Servings: 1
Proteins/Carbs/Fats: 2 / 2 / 0

Ingredients

1/2 cup Seedless Green or Purple Grapes (washed)

1 Apple (your choice, cored and chopped, I leave the skin on)

1/4 cup Walnuts

1 stalk Celery (chopped)

To Taste Sea Salt and Pepper

1 tsp Lemon Juice (to help apple from turning brown)

To Taste Isabel's Homemade Mayonnaise (see Dressings section), or Greek Yogurt

Directions

Mix all ingredients together and enjoy.

Add mayonnaise or yogurt as dressing. Mix, and enjoy!

Submitted By: Karen - Luling, Louisiana

Sweet Potato Salad with Orange and Lime

Servings: 8
Proteins/Carbs/Fats: 0 / 2 / 3

Ingredients

2 tsp Grated Lime Rind

1/4 cup Fresh Lime Juice

2 tsp Grated Orange Rind

1/4 cup Fresh Orange Juice

3 lbs Sweet Potatoes (peeled and cut into 3/4 inch cubes)

1/4 cup Fresh Snipped Chives

1/2 cup Olive Oil

2 tsp Dijon Mustard

Directions

Whisk fruit juices and rinds with mustard and oil.

Steam sweet potato cubes, covered, for about 7 minutes or until just tender. Toss with dressing. Cool and add chives, salt and pepper to taste. Toss well.

Submitted By: Dianne L. – Clinton Township, Michigan

Potato Salad

Servings: 6
Proteins/Carbs/Fats: 1 / 2 / 1

Ingredients

4 Hard-Boiled Eggs (diced)

2 cups Pickles (diced)

2 cups Boneless Roasted Chicken Breast (diced)

1 Small Green Apple (sliced and diced)

2 Small Boiled Potatoes (diced)

1/4 Steamed Cauliflower Head (diced)

2 cups Frozen Peas

4 Tbsp Isabel's Homemade Mayonnaise (see Dressings section)

To taste Salt

Directions

Combine diced eggs, pickles, chicken, apple, potatoes and cauliflower in a large serving bowl. Toss to mix well.

Add frozen peas, mayonnaise and salt. Toss again, very carefully.

This salad may be served immediately or on the next day.

Makes 6 to 8 servings.

Submitted By: Sofia P. – San Francisco Bay Area, California

Apple-Celery-Raisin Salad

Servings: 4
Proteins/Carbs/Fats: 0 / 1 / 1

Ingredients

1 Apple

1 stalk Celery

1 cup Raisins

Isabel's Homemade Mayonnaise (see Dressings section)

Directions

Cut apple and celery stalk into small pieces.

Combine apple, celery, and raisins in a bowl. Stir in mayonnaise to make the mixture the desired consistency.

Submitted By: Corinda L.

Hot Salads

Roasted California Salad

Servings: 5
Proteins/Carbs/Fats: 1 / 2 / 1

Ingredients

1 Red Pepper (cut into spears or bite-sized pieces)

1 Orange Pepper (cut into spears)

8 Asparagus Spears (cut into 2 inch pieces)

1/2 Medium Squash (sliced at an angle about 1/4 inch thick)

1/2 Medium Zucchini (sliced at angle about 1/4 inch thick)

1 cup Baby Portabellas (sliced, including the stems)

1 Small Red Onion (sliced into 8 sections, optional)

1 tsp Salt

1 tsp Black Pepper

2 cloves Garlic (finely chopped)

1 tsp Rosemary

2 Tbsp Coconut Oil

1 cup Strawberries (quartered)

1 Mango (sliced into 1/4 inch sections)

1 Avocado (sliced into 1/4 inch sections)

1 cup Walnut Halves

1 head Red Romaine Lettuce, Mesclun, Mixed Greens, etc.

Directions

Preheat oven to 400° F. Prepare veggies.

Prepare seasoning for veggies. Coat veggies in seasoning, and loosely cover with foil on a cookie sheet. Roast for 40 minutes. Turn once.

While veggies roast, prepare Rosemary Lemon Vinaigrette (refer to recipe in the Dressing section).

Prepare strawberries, mango, avocado, and walnuts.

Wash and prepare lettuce.

Create your Roasted California Salad! Place lettuce in a large serving bowl. Pile the roasted veggies atop lettuce in the middle of your most beautiful serving dish. Add fruit, avocado, nuts along the sides of the dish.

Submitted By: Emily P. - Saint Louis, Missouri

Grilled Asparagus Salad

Servings: 5
Proteins/Carbs/Fats: 0 / 2 / 2

Ingredients

1/4 cup Olive Oil

1/8 cup Lemon Juice

12 Fresh Asparagus Spears

6 cups Fresh Spinach Leaves

1/8 cup Grated Parmesan Cheese

1/4-1/2 Red Onion (thinly sliced)

1/2-1 oz Raw Almond Slivers

8-10 Cherry Tomatoes (halved)

Directions

Preheat oven to 350º F.

Combine olive oil and lemon juice.

Coat asparagus spears with olive oil/lemon juice mixture reserving excess mixture for dressing. Place on cookie sheet and place in oven for approximately 15 minutes. Can grill them if you desire.

In a large bowl, combine spinach, parmesan cheese, onions, almond slivers and cherry tomatoes.

Cut asparagus into bite sized pieces and add to bowl along with extra olive oil mixture for dressing. Toss and serve.

Submitted By: Vicki F. - Springfield, Missouri

Warm Chickpea, Pumpkin, and Spinach Salad

Servings: 6
Proteins/Carbs/Fats: 0 / 2 / 1

Ingredients

3 cups Pumpkin (peeled and cut into 3/4 inch pieces)

1-2 Tbsp Extra Virgin Olive Oil

1 Red Onion (thinly sliced)

1 clove Garlic (chopped)

1 bunch English Spinach (trimmed)

1/4 tsp Ground Nutmeg

1/4 tsp Cayenne Pepper

1 Orange (for juice)

14 oz can Chickpeas (rinsed)

1/2 cup Feta Cheese (crumbled) or Shaved Parmesan or Shaved Jarlsburg

Mesclun, Mixed Greens, etc.

Directions

Cook pumpkin (peeled and cut into 3/4-inch pieces) until tender (about 6-7 minutes). Drain.

Heat 1-2 tablespoons of extra virgin olive oil in a large frying pan over medium heat. Add red onion and garlic and cook for 3-4 minutes or until onion is soft. Add English spinach, ground nutmeg and cayenne pepper, and stir. Add pumpkin and juice of orange and cook, stirring occasionally, for 2-3 minutes. Stir in chickpeas and cheese of choice.

Serve. Enjoy

Submitted By: Annie L.

Scrambled Eggs Salad

Servings: 4
Proteins/Carbs/Fats: 1 / 1 / 1

Ingredients

3 Large Organic Eggs

2 cups Mushrooms (diced)

1 Tbsp Butter

1/2 tsp Ground Black Pepper

1/2 tsp Garlic Powder

1/2 tsp Celtic Sea Salt

1/2 tsp Dried Parsley

1/2 cup Celery (finely diced)

1/2 cup Yellow Pepper (finely diced)

1/2 cup Red Pepper (finely diced)

1/2 cup Cherry Tomatoes (chopped)

8 cup Crispy Salad Mix

Directions

Heat butter in a frying pan over medium heat. After butter is melted, add mushrooms and sauté until golden brown (5 minutes). Remove from heat. Beat the eggs and whisk them in a bowl. Add salt, pepper and garlic powder. Pour eggs over the mushrooms and put back to heat. Stir the eggs frequently till set.

Make a bed of salad on your plate with the salad mix, diced peppers, celery and tomatoes (dressing optional). Place scrambled eggs in the middle of the salad bed and season with dried parsley.

Enjoy!

Submitted By: Judit - Hungary

Warm Potatoes, Shallots, Beets, and Endive Salad

Ingredients

Cooked and still warm (not hot) Potatoes

Shallots (chopped)

Red Beets (cooked, cold, sliced)

Endive (cut in 1/2 inch laces)

Vinegar

Olive Oil

To taste Salt and Pepper

*Amounts of each ingredient will vary depending on desired portions.

Directions

Slice potatoes, and put in a bowl with vinegar and olive oil, salt and pepper, and chopped shallots.

Add beets and endive to the mix.

Serve with poached chicken, or by itself.

Submitted By: Sarah H.

Roasted Vegetable Salad

Servings: 8
Proteins/Carbs/Fats: 0 / 1 / 2

Ingredients

2 cups Asparagus (cut into 2 inch pieces)

2 cups Button Mushrooms or Small Portabella Mushrooms

12 Cherry Tomatoes

To taste Salt and Pepper

6 Tbsp Olive Oil (divided)

3 Tbsp Red Wine Vinegar

2 Tbsp Minced Shallots

1-2 Tbsp Prepared Horseradish

1 Tbsp Honey

Directions

Preheat oven to 400° F.

Prepare vegetables and spread on a baking sheet. Drizzle with salt, pepper, and two tablespoons of olive oil.

Roast ten minutes or until tomato skins split and mushrooms are browned.

Whisk together remaining ingredients and pour over hot roasted vegetables. Serve, and enjoy!

Submitted By: Virginia H.

Warm Tandoori Chicken Salad

Servings: 4
Proteins/Carbs/Fats: 3 / 2 / 0

Ingredients

2 Chicken Breasts or Thighs

1 tsp Olive Oil

1/2 cup Low Fat Plain Greek Yogurt

2 tsp Tandoori Spice Mix Powder or Paste (or to taste)

To taste Salt and Pepper

1 bag Mixed Lettuce Leaves or Baby Spinach Leaves

1 Red Onion

1 Cucumber

1 Red Bell Pepper

1 Green Bell Pepper

1 Tomato

2 sticks Celery

1/4 cup Raw Cashews or Peanuts (chopped or whole)

Directions

Dice chicken and cook in coconut oil. Towards end of cooking add the paste or spice powder. Turn off heat and mix through yogurt. Add salt/pepper to taste.

Arrange salad leaves on serving platter or split between 4 bowls.

Dice all vegetables and spread over leaves.

Mix chicken yogurt into salad and sprinkle with nuts.

Can also be served cold in summer – cook chicken prior and allow to cool, and then mix with vegetables.

Submitted By: Lisa C. – Melbourne, Victoria, Australia

Barbecue Veggie Salad

Servings: 2
Proteins/Carbs/Fats: 0 / 2 / 1

Ingredients

1/4 cup Barbecued Onions

1 cup Broccoli (cut into small florets or slivers, lightly steamed)

1/2 cup Cauliflower (broken into tiny florets, lightly steamed)

2 Tbsp Carrots (finely grated)

2 Tbsp Red Cabbage (finely grated)

2 Tbsp Yellow Squash (finely grated)

1 Tbsp Isabel's Homemade Mayonnaise (see Dressings section)

3 thin slivers of Dill Pickle

1/2 cup Lettuce (finely shredded)

1/2 cup Alfalfa Sprouts

2 slices Avocado

Directions

To make barbecued onions, sauté one small white onion in butter until it begins to soften. Add ½ tablespoon of barbecue sauce and continue sautéing, stirring frequently until onion is thoroughly wilted.

To make salad, gently combine all ingredients and serve.

Any other vegetables can be added, to make a dish that is never the same twice!

This warm salad is also yummy in toasted snackwiches, wraps, or pita breads!

Submitted By: Maz P.

Leafy Greens & Bacon

Servings: 4
Proteins/Carbs/Fats: 2 / 1 / 2

Ingredients

1/4-1/2 Red Pepper (chopped)
1 Red Onion (chopped)
6-8 slices Bacon
1 package Baby Leaf Spinach
1 package Frozen Brussels Sprouts
1/2-1 cup Parmesan Cheese
Beef Bouillon Granules

Directions

Use a 10-inch skillet to fry the bacon. Place the bacon on paper towels to drain. Break bacon into 1-inch pieces and lay aside.

Drain skillet from bacon grease; then sauté red pepper and onion until crunchy. Add spinach, bacon, and bouillon. Cook a little longer.

Add brussels sprouts to the skillet and stir well. While in skillet, cut each brussels sprout in half.

Add parmesan cheese and stir.

*To cook brussels sprouts: Boil in slightly salted water for about 15 minutes (no need to thaw them first).

Submitted By: Laura B.

Mixed Vegetables

Tomato Chevre Salad

Servings: 4
Proteins/Carbs/Fats: 0 / 2 / 3

Ingredients

2 cups Spring Lettuce

4-6 Ripe Tomatoes

1/2 Red Onion (finely chopped)

8-10 Basil Leaves

2-3 oz Chevre (goat cheese)

4 oz Olive Oil

2 oz Rice Wine Vinegar

Salt & Pepper

Directions

Chop red onion. Dice tomatoes.

Put onion and tomatoes in a bowl; add the oil, vinegar, salt and pepper. Let marinate for 30 minutes.

When ready to serve, lay lettuce on a plate.

Chop basil and sprinkle it over the lettuce.

Stir the tomato mixture and spoon it out onto the lettuce.

Crumble chevre and sprinkle it over the salad.

Fresh, delicious and ready to serve.

Submitted By: Jeanet L.

Fresh Garden Salad

Ingredients

Romaine Lettuce

Green Onions

Green Pepper

Cucumbers

Tomatoes

Avocados

Mushrooms

Celery

Carrots

Turkey Breast or Chicken Breast (optional)

Directions

Adjust amount of each ingredient to taste.

Toss all vegetables together.

Add turkey or chicken, if desired.

Serve with the dressing of your choice, and enjoy.

Use vegetables from your garden for the most delicious salad!

Submitted By: Tim S.

Garlic Pepper Salad

Servings: 8
Proteins/Carbs/Fats: 0 / 1 / 1

Ingredients

4 Large Peppers of Assorted Colors (diced)

1 cup Celery (chopped)

1 cup Carrots (chopped)

1 cup Black Olives (sliced)

1 cup Artichoke Hearts (quartered)

2-3 cloves Fresh Garlic (minced)

To taste Sea Salt

Extra Virgin Olive Oil

Directions

Chop peppers and other ingredients (you can add or delete whatever suits your fancy) and add to bowl. Add minced garlic and gently toss. Sprinkle with Sea Salt to taste and drizzle with Olive Oil. Chill for a few hours to enhance flavors.

This salad is always a hit and the natural flavors of the peppers, garlic and other ingredients are plenty without any additional flavors added.

Serves 6 to 8 or more depending on other side dishes!

Submitted By: Kate C. – Binghamton, NY

www.BeyondDiet.com

Palm, Pepper, Tomato, Artichoke, and Olive Salad

Servings: 4
Proteins/Carbs/Fats: 0 / 2 / 0

Ingredients

1 can Hearts of Palm (drained)

1 Whole Roasted Red Pepper (sliced)

1/2 jar Sun Dried Tomatoes (drained)

1 can Quartered Artichokes (drained)

1 cup Green Olives Stuffed with Garlic or Blue Cheese

1/2 cup Capers and Fresh Chopped Basil (to your liking)

Romaine Lettuce

Directions

Mix all ingredients together, and throw it on top of some baby romaine.

Top with the dressing of your choice, and enjoy!

Submitted By: Maryanne D.

Chopped Cucumber and Pepper Salad

Servings: 2
Proteins/Carbs/Fats: 0 / 2 / 1

Ingredients

2 Seedless Cucumbers

1 Small Yellow, Orange, or Red Bell Pepper

1 Tbsp Extra Virgin Olive Oil

1 Tbsp Red Wine Vinegar

1 pinch Salt

To Taste Freshly Ground Pepper

1 Tbsp Fresh Basil (leaves stacked, cut into shreds)

Directions

Quarter the cucumbers lengthwise. Then cut them into 1/2-inch pieces.

Core the peppers and remove the seeds. Then cut them into 1/2-inch wide strips.

Mix together extra virgin olive oil, vinegar, salt and pepper.

Toss together cucumber and bell pepper.

Add olive oil mix and fresh basil, and toss again.

Submitted By: Cameille T. – Trincity, Trinidad & Tobago

Anything Goes Sprouted Salad

Ingredients

Mixed Greens with Lots of Variety (dandelion, radicchio, arugula, baby romaine, baby spinach)

Fresh Dill

Broccoli and/or Cauliflower

Sprouted Mung Beans and Marrowfat Peas

1 Tbsp Hemp Seeds

1 Tbsp Flax Seed Oil

2 Tbsp Apple Cider Vinegar

1 tsp Italian Seasoning

1/2 tsp Lemon Juice (fresh is best)

Directions

Toss together mixed greens, dill, broccoli, cauliflower, beans, peas and hemp seeds.

Combine oil, vinegar, Italian seasoning and lemon juice. Pour mixture over greens, and toss.

If you want to add some protein to this salad, it goes very well with a boneless chicken breast or a piece of grilled Pacific salmon.

Submitted By: Michelle M.

Surprise Salad

Servings: 6
Proteins/Carbs/Fats: 0 / 2 / 2

Ingredients

1 head Romaine Lettuce

3 Carrots (grated or shredded)

1 Small Onion (or 3-4 table onions, or a handful of chives chopped small)

1/3 stalk Celery Including the Leafy Ends (cut into thin slices, about 1/8-inch thick)

Add as available:

3 Small Beets (peeled and shredded)

4 Radishes (sliced thin)

2 Small Leeks (including tops, sliced thin)

1/2 cup Pea Pods, sliced in 1/4- to 1/2-inch pieces.

Dressing:

4 Tbsp Apple Cider Vinegar

2 Tbsp Water

1/2 cup + 2 Tbsp Extra Virgin Olive Oil

1 Tbsp Crushed Dried Herbs (optional)

Directions

Create base salad by mixing two groups of ingredients together. Fill salad bowls. Top with whatever is available in your kitchen: shredded zucchini, diced green pepper, diced avocado, cottage cheese, shredded cheese, sliced or diced hard-boiled eggs, canned or leftover chicken/salmon/tuna, chick peas, kidney beans, peas, green beans, diced tomatoes, thinly sliced cucumber, sunflower seeds, pumpkin seeds, sesame seeds, pine nuts, chopped nuts.

Combine dressing ingredients. Shake well before drizzling on salad.

*Place leftover base salad in Zip Lock bag. Pack to bottom and begin rolling bag tightly to expel all excess air. Zip closed. Store in crisper. This salad can remain fresh for at least five days if stored without excess air. When salad base is used again the next day, air must be squeezed out again before leftover salad is put back in the refrigerator.

Submitted By: Virginia

Sauerkraut Salad

Servings: 5
Proteins/Carbs/Fats: 2 / 3 / 0

Ingredients

48 oz Sauerkraut (drained, rinsed and chopped)

4 ribs Celery (thinly sliced)

1 Large (or 2 Medium) Sweet Onions (Walla Walla or Vidalia, sliced thin)

2 Red Peppers (seeded, broiled and skin removed, sliced thin)

2 Carrots (peeled and grated)

2 Apples (grated, leave peel on if they are fresh and not bruised)

1 Green Pepper (seeded and sliced thin)

2 tsp Celery Seed

1/4 tsp Pepper

1 3/4 cup Stevia (to taste)

6-8 Tbsp Apple Cider Vinegar (or whatever vinegar you have on hand)

1 cup Pecans (chopped)

Directions

Mix vinegar, celery seed, and stevia; heat to dissolve stevia. Pour mixture over all ingredients. Mix well. Let stand in the refrigerator overnight before serving.

This recipe makes a very crunchy crisp salad!

This salad will keep for several days.

Submitted By: Sam S.

Tomato and Cucumber Salad

Servings: 4
Proteins/Carbs/Fats: 0 / 2 / 0

Ingredients

5 Tomatoes (diced)

1 Onion (finely chopped)

1 Cucumber (sliced)

1 Green Pepper (chopped)

1 handful Basil (chopped)

1 handful Parsley (chopped)

6 cloves Garlic (finely chopped, optional)

2 Tbsp White Wine Vinegar

To Taste Salt and Freshly Ground Black Pepper

Directions

Combine all ingredients in a large bowl.

Toss well, seasoning to taste with salt and pepper.

Chill before serving.

Submitted By: Annie L.

Asparagus, Roasted Red Pepper, and Arugula Salad

Servings: 4
Proteins/Carbs/Fats: 0 / 2 / 0

Ingredients

1 bunch (about 1 pound) Asparagus (trimmed)

5 oz (about 4 cups) Baby Arugula

1 Roasted Bell Pepper (thinly sliced, about 1/2 cup)

1/3 cup Kalamata Olives (pitted and finely chopped)

1/2 Small Red Onion (finely chopped)

White Balsamic & Dijon Mustard Vinaigrette (see Dressings section)

Directions

Bring a medium pot of water to a boil. Add asparagus, cook until vibrant green and crisp tender, 1-1 1/2 min. Drain asparagus, immerse in ice water bath to stop the cooking process. Drain again, set aside.

To roast the pepper, heat grill to high heat. Lay pepper on the grill, cook until well charred. Rotate the pepper a quarter turn and repeat until each side is well charred. Place the charred, hot pepper in a resealable bag. Seal and steam until cooled to room temperature (about 30 minutes) Remove the skin. Gently pull the pepper apart and remove and discard the seeds and stems. Thinly slice.

On each plate, place a bed of Baby Arugula. Layer asparagus on top. Arrange the roasted pepper on top of the asparagus. Generously drizzle with the vinaigrette to taste. Garnish with olives and red onion.

Submitted By: Susie M.

Calico Salad

Servings: 5
Proteins/Carbs/Fats: 0 / 3 / 0

Ingredients

16 oz can non-GMO Corn

14.5 oz can French Style Green Beans

1 cup Red (orange or yellow) Pepper (diced or chopped)

1 cup Celery (diced or chopped)

2 bunches Green Onions (sliced thin or chopped)

1 cup Red Onion (about 1/2 onion, diced)

1 (or less) Hot House Cucumber (diced)

4 oz jar Diced Pimento (drained, optional)

Directions

Drain canned corn and green beans. Combine corn, green beans, peppers, celery, onions and cucumber in a large bowl. Add pimento, if desired. Toss together.

Pour dressing over vegetables. Toss to coat. Cover and refrigerate overnight to marinate.

Submitted By: Marilyn S. – Myrtle Point, Oregon

Mixed Veggies with Lemon Dressing

Servings: 6
Proteins/Carbs/Fats: 0 / 3 / 2

Ingredients

8 Ripe Plum Tomatoes

6 Celery Stalks

3 Peppers (preferably a mix of yellow, orange and red)

1 Small Red Onion

2 (6 oz) jars Marinated Artichokes

1 cup Kalamata Olives (pitted)

1/2 cup Fresh Dill (coarsely chopped)

1 Lemon

2 tsp Dijon Mustard

2 Large Garlic Cloves (minced)

2 tsp Dried Dillweed

1/2 tsp Dried Basil

1/2 tsp Sea Salt

To Taste Freshly Ground Pepper

1/3 cup Olive Oil

Directions

Cut tomatoes in half. Squeeze out and discard seeds and juice, then coarsely chop. Thinly slice celery diagonally. Slice peppers into bite size strips. Cut onion in half then thinly slice. Place all in a large bowl, separating into rings.

Drain artichokes well, then coarsely chop. Remove peel from oranges. Slice oranges in half crosswise, then into thick half moons. Add both to salad with olives and ½ cup chopped fresh dill.

Squeeze ¼ cup juice from lemon into a small bowl. Whisk Dijon, garlic, dried dillweed, basil, salt and pepper. Slowly whisk in oil.

Before serving, drizzle lemon juice mix over vegetables and toss. After dressing, the salad stands up well at room temperature for several hours or in the refrigerator about half a day.

Garnish with fresh dill sprigs.

Submitted By: Connie

Post's Lettuce-less Salad

Servings: 4
Proteins/Carbs/Fats: 0 / 1 / 2

Ingredients

1 Medium Red Onion

1 Medium Sweet Pepper (any color)

1 Large Cucumber (peeled or not)

1 Medium Tomato

8 oz Hard Cheddar Cheese (raw)

Directions

Cube all ingredients into 1/2-inch cubes or, preferably, smaller. Do not use a food processor – it must be cut by hand to work properly.

Mix all ingredients together in a large bowl. Cover and place in the refrigerator overnight. The juices will come out of some of the veggies and meld together for a beautiful and flavorful ready-made dressing. (No separate dressing is necessary.)

Variations: Add celery or carrot or both.

Use several colors of sweet pepper to make it more eye-catching. A handful of raw nuts can add fat, or some cubed chicken or turkey breast can add a lean protein.

Use this salad as a relish to replace more calorie rich condiments.

Leftovers can also be added to soup.

Submitted By: John and Angela P.

Oriental Salads

Asian Stir-fry Salad with Curry Lentils

Servings: 6
Proteins/Carbs/Fats: 0 / 2 / 2

Ingredients

Stir-Fry
1 head Broccoli
1 head Bok Choy
1/2 head Cabbage
1 or 2 handfuls Carrots
1 or 2 handfuls Mushrooms

Dressing
To taste Sea Salt, Pepper, and Oriental Seasoning
1 Lemon (juiced)
a few Tbsps Olive Oil
2-3 splashes Nama Shoyu/ Braggs Liquid Amino
1/4 cup Honey
1 piece Ginger
1 clove Garlic

Lentils:
1 cup Lentils
2 1/2 cups Water
2 Beef Bouillon Cubes
1 Bay Leaf
1 tsp Salt
1/4 cup Butter
1 Large Onion (chopped)
1 clove Garlic (minced)
1 tsp Sea Salt
1-2 Tbsp Curry Powder

Directions

Put all stir-fry ingredients in the food processor and process until everything is well chopped.

Put all dressing ingredients in the blender, and blend till smooth. Dress the salad, and add sesame seeds.

Bring to a boil and simmer 20 minutes: lentils, water, beef bouillon cubes, bay leaf, and salt.

Meanwhile, in a pan, sauté together: butter, onion, and garlic. After that, add sea salt and curry powder to the pan.

Fry it briefly, then add the lentils, stir everything together, and serve on top of the raw stir fry.

Submitted By: Christina R. – Kyoto, Japan

Teriyaki Ginger Mushrooms

Servings: 4
Proteins/Carbs/Fats: 0 / 2 / 0

Ingredients

2 Tbsp Coconut Oil

4 Spring Onions (sliced)

2 cloves Garlic (crushed)

1 tsp Fresh Ginger (finely chopped)

2 1/2 - 3 cups Small Button Mushrooms

1/3 cup Honey or Teriyaki Sauce

Directions

Heat a wok over high heat until hot. Add coconut oil. Add 3 of the spring onions and garlic and stir-fry for 1 minute. Add ginger and stir-fry for 30 seconds.

Add mushrooms and stir-fry for 1 - 2 minutes until mushrooms begin to soften. Add teriyaki sauce and stir-fry for 2 minutes or until mushrooms are glossy and just tender. Top with the last spring onion, sliced diagonally.

Serve with jasmine rice and steamed greens, or as a side dish with barbecue lamb, chicken or sausages.

Submitted By: Mary B.

Thai Chicken Salad

Ingredients

Lean Chicken Breasts or Thighs

Lettuce Mix

Cherry Tomatoes (or other kind of tomato)

Cucumber

Red or Orange Peppers

Red Onion or Shallots

Coconut Oil

Thai Spices (chili, lemongrass, cumin, turmeric, etc. – or can buy as Thai seasoning)

Garlic

Ginger

Sea Salt

Almonds or Cashews

Directions

Dice chicken. Sauté in coconut oil with spices, ginger and garlic.

Make salad with remaining ingredients.

Toss warm chicken over salad with almonds.

Serve with brown rice.

Submitted By: Angela L.

Chinese Spinach Salad

Servings: 8
Proteins/Carbs/Fats: 0 / 2 / 0

Ingredients

2 cups Cooked Brown Rice

1 bag Spinach (washed)

1 bag Bean Sprouts

3-6 sticks Celery (cut in small pieces)

1/2 cup Raisins

1 cup Fresh Mushrooms (sliced)

1 Green Pepper (or 1/2 red and 1/2 green, for color)

2 sprigs Parsley

1/2 cup Green Onions

1/2 cup Sunflower Seeds

Tamari Olive Oil Sauce (see Dressings section)

Directions

Combine rice, spinach, bean sprouts, celery, mushrooms, peppers, and green onions in a large bowl.

Add raisins and sunflower seeds.

Garnish with parsley.

About 1 ½ - 2 hours before serving, pour sauce over dressing.

This makes a big salad – it is a great recipe to bring to a potluck!

Submitted By: J. Doiron – Saint John, New Brunswick, Canada

Bokin' Awesome Salad

Servings: 2
Proteins/Carbs/Fats: 0 / 2 / 0

Ingredients

1 cup Bok Choy
1/2 cup Carrots (chopped)
1/2 cup Sweet Peas
1/2 cup Mushrooms
1/4 cup Onions
1 Tbsp Garlic (minced)
1/2 tsp Cayenne Pepper
To taste Pepper
2-3 Tbsp Coconut Oil
(optional)
1/2 cup Water

Directions

Heat large skillet or wok. Pour in 1/3 of the water (to keep from burning the skillet). Keep adding water as needed throughout the recipe.

Add carrots first, stir until slightly tender. Then add mushrooms, peas, onions, garlic and tofu. Cook till tender.

Last, add the bok choy, coconut oil (optional) and cayenne pepper.

When the bok choy looks slightly wilted, turn off the stove. Let cool for a bit, then serve warm.

Submitted By: Katie B. – Kariya, Japan

Quinoa Salads

Quinoa Salad with Apples and Almonds

Servings: 4
Proteins/Carbs/Fats: 1 / 2 / 2

Ingredients

1 cup Quinoa

2 cups Water

2 Tbsp Honey

1/4 cup Lemon Juice

1/2 tsp Kosher Salt

3 Tbsp Olive Oil

1 cup Tart Apple (peeled and diced)

1 cup Celery (finely chopped)

1/3 cup Raisins

1/3 cup Parsley (chopped)

1/2 cup Almonds (coarsely chopped)

Directions

Rinse quinoa and bring to a boil. Turn head down and simmer for about 15 minutes, until water is absorbed. Fluff with fork and allow to cool.

In a small bowl, mix honey, lemon juice, and salt. Add oil slowly

Add all other ingredients and mix.

Enjoy!

Submitted By: Jeanne M. - Kennedy Saskatchewan Canada

Quinoa, Black Bean, and Corn Salad

Servings: 4
Proteins/Carbs/Fats: 0 / 1 / 2

Ingredients

2 Tbsp Juice from 1/2 Lemon

1/4 cup Olive Oil

2 Tbsp Minced Cilantro (may substitute Italian seasoning)

To taste Sea Salt

1 cup non-GMO corn (simmer until tender; 1/2 cup cooking liquid reserved)

1/2 cup Quinoa (rinsed thoroughly)

1/4 tsp Cumin Seeds

1/2 cup Canned Black Beans (rinsed)

1 Medium Tomato (diced small)

2 Tbsp Red Onion (minced)

Directions

Mix first 3 ingredients plus 1/2 teaspoon salt in a small non-reactive bowl; set aside this dressing.

Bring corn cooking liquid to a boil in a small saucepan. Add quinoa and cumin; cover and simmer until quinoa absorbs the liquid and is tender, about 10 minutes. Transfer quinoa to a large non-reactive bowl; cool slightly. Then add corn, remaining ingredients, and dressing; toss to combine. Chill.

Makes 4 servings

Submitted By: Don P.

Black Quinoa Salad with Salmon

Servings: 3
Proteins/Carbs/Fats: 2 / 2 / 1

Ingredients

1 Salmon Steak (cooked, boned, and flaked)

1/2 cup Black Quinoa

2 cloves Garlic (finely chopped)

1 Medium Onion (finely chopped)

1 Tbsp Butter

1 Medium Carrot (grated)

1 bunch Fresh Coriander

1/3 tsp Cumin

To taste Salt, Pepper & Dry Ginger

2 Fresh Peppers (1 red, 1 orange)

Za'atar (middle-eastern blend of herbs with thyme and sesame seeds)

Directions

Boil the quinoa in a little water with the oil, salt, and cumin. Drain, and set aside.

Warm the butter gently in a large frying pan. Add the garlic, onion, and carrot. Cut some fresh coriander into the pan. Add the drained quinoa, and mix well. Season to taste with a little salt, pepper, and/or ginger. Stir in the salmon flakes and mix well.

Heap the mixture onto a large, salad plate, and decorate with long and slender strips of red and orange pepper.

Cool and enjoy!

Submitted By: Debbie G.- Israel

Quinoa Mango Salad

Servings: 3
Proteins/Carbs/Fats: 1 / 2 / 2

Ingredients

1 cup Quinoa

2 cups Water

1/4 tsp Salt

1 Mango (peeled and cubed)

1/2 cup Cucumber (cut in 1/2-inch cubes)

1/4 cup Blanched Almonds

2 Tbsp Roasted Pumpkin Seeds

Dressing:

1 tsp Ghee (clarified butter)

1 tsp Turmeric

1 Lime or 1/2 Lemon (juiced)

2 Tbsp Olive Oil

2 Tbsp Fresh Cilantro (chopped)

To Taste Salt and Freshly Ground Black Pepper

Directions

Wash quinoa and boil in water for 10 minutes, Let sit until quinoa absorbs all the water. Fluff with a fork and let it cool to room temperature.

Combine the mango, cucumber, almonds and pumpkin seeds in a salad bowl.

To make the dressing, heat Ghee in a small pan and fry with turmeric for 30 seconds, then let it cool. Add the lemon or juice. Mix in olive oil, cilantro, salt and pepper.

Add the cooled quinoa to the mango mixture, pour the dressing over the salad, and toss.

Submitted By: Nicki G. – Gabriola, British Columbia, Canada

Chickpea Quinoa Salad

Servings: 4
Proteins/Carbs/Fats: 2 / 3 / 2

Ingredients

2 cups Canned Chickpeas
(drained well in running water)

2 cups Cooked Quinoa
(cooled)

1/2 cup Celery (finely
chopped)

1/2 cup Shallots (finely
chopped)

1 cup English Cucumber
(diced)

1 Avocado (medium firm,
diced)

1 cup Raw Pumpkin Seeds

1/2 cup Unsweetened Large
Flakes of Coconut

1/2 cup Dried Cranberry

1/2 tsp Roasted Cumin
Powder (optional)

Dressing:
2 Tbsp Apple Cider Vinegar
2 Tbsp Extra Virgin Olive Oil
1/2 tsp Celtic Salt
2 tsp Honey (optional

Directions

Mix the first set of ingredients
together in a large bowl.

Whisk together dressing
ingredients. Pour mixture into
the salad, and toss well.

Serves 4 to 6

Submitted By: Molly M. – Mississauga, Ontario, Canada

Warm Quinoa Salad

Servings: 4
Proteins/Carbs/Fats: 1 / 1 / 0

Ingredients

1/2 cup Quinoa

1 cup Organic Chicken/
Vegetable Stock or Water

1/2 cup Walnuts

1 Sweet Potato (cubed)

1 cup Pumpkin (cubed)

2 cups Baby Spinach (roughly
torn)

Olive Oil & Lemon Juice
Dressing (see Dressings
section)

Directions

Roast the pumpkin and sweet
potato with some coconut oil
until tender

Bring stock/water and quinoa
to the boil, cover and simmer
for 10-15 minutes or until the
liquid is mostly absorbed.
Remove from heat.

Fluff quinoa with fork and
stir through the torn spinach.
Replace the lid and leave for a
few minutes until the spinach
is nicely wilted.

In a large bowl mix the quinoa
and spinach with the roasted
vegetables.

Pour on dressing and toss.

Lovely served warm but also
nice cold.

Enjoy!!

Kale Quinoa Salad

Servings: 3
Proteins/Carbs/Fats: 0 / 1 / 2

Ingredients

1 bunch Kale (chopped small)

1 cup Cooked Quinoa

2 Tbsp Daikon Radish (grated)

3 Green Onions (chopped) or 1/4 medium White Onion (chopped small)

2 Tbsp Ground Seed & Nut Mix

2-3 Tbsp Olive Oil

2-3 Tbsp Apple Cider Vinegar or Lemon Juice

2 Tbsp Lime Juice

1/2 tsp Ginger (2 dry knuckles, ground)

3-4 twists Ground Black Pepper

1 Tbsp Stevia

1-2 Tbsp Tahini (sesame butter)

*Pictured Salad substituted tomatoes for radishes.

Directions

To make ground seed and nut mix:

Use a coffee grinder and mix almonds, cashews, pumpkin, sesame, flax, sunflower, etc.

Mix olive oil, juices, ginger, black pepper, Stevia, and tahini together. Stir in with quinoa.

Combine all salad ingredients and quinoa mix. Sprinkle seed and nut mix on top.

Makes a great lunch with some sliced tomato!

Submitted By: Dave C.

In-the-Fridge Salad

Servings: 1
Proteins/Carbs/Fats: 2 / 3 / 1

Ingredients

Quinoa (enough for one person, pre-cook and take out of the freezer the night before)

2 pieces Turkey Bacon

6 Cherry Tomatoes (halved)

3" Cucumber (peeled and cubed)

1 Yellow Pepper (cubed)

1 Tbsp Hummus with Lemon & Coriander

To taste Ground Black Pepper and Sea Salt

2 Asparagus Spears

1 tsp Butter

Directions

Cook the turkey bacon and asparagus in butter until cooked. When done, cut the turkey bacon into squares.

Place all other ingredients in a bowl and mix.

Add turkey bacon and asparagus spears on top, and enjoy!

Submitted By: Margaret W. – Devon, United Kingdom

Salads With Avocado

Avocado, Cucumber, Mango, & Sultanas Salad

Servings: 5
Proteins/Carbs/Fats: 1 / 1 / 1

Ingredients

1 Avocado

1/2 cup Cucumber

1 Mango

1/4 cup Sultanas

1/4 cup Pine-Nuts and/or Walnuts (chopped)

1 Yellow Pepper (diced)

1/2 cup Cooked King Prawns (chickpeas for vegetarians)

1/2 cup Natural Yogurt

1 tsp Raw Honey

1 handle Mint (roughly chopped)

1 Tbsp Balsamic Vinegar

1 tsp Dijon Mustard

1 pinch Salt

To taste Roughly Ground Black Pepper

Directions

Roughly chop the cucumber, mango and avocado into a bowl. Add the sultanas, nuts, pepper, and prawns.

Separately, stir into the yogurt the mustard, honey and vinegar. Then add the mint, salt and pepper.

Toss the yogurt mix with the salad until lightly coated. For extra flavor grate a little lemon zest over the top.

Submitted By: Agnes L.

Biltong Salad

Servings: 2
Proteins/Carbs/Fats: 4 / 3 / 3

Ingredients

1 Cucumber (sliced)

1 packet Arugula & Watercress

1 Avocado

1 Salad Yellow Pepper

1 Punnet Rosa Tomato

1 Ripe Mango (sliced)

8 oz (200g) Moist Beef Biltong (sliced)

2 oz (60g) Feta Cheese

Directions

Toss together all the salad ingredients.

Serve the salad with a tzatziki dressing.

Enjoy!

Submitted By: Elmarie E. - South Africa

JJ Salad

Servings: 4
Proteins/Carbs/Fats: 1 / 1 / 2

Ingredients

1/2 head Fresh Lettuce (torn or shredded)

1/2 English Cucumber (sliced)

1 Small Onion (sliced)

1/2 Red Pepper (chopped)

1/2 Yellow Pepper (chopped)

3/4-1 cup Mini Italian Tomatoes (halved)

1/2-3/4 cup White Button Mushrooms (sliced)

1 Large Avocado (cubed)

1/2-3/4 cup Feta Cheese (cubed)

3-4 Jumbo Free Range Eggs (hard boiled and sliced)

Directions

Layer the ingredients in a large salad bowl.

Chill and serve.

Sprinkle with parsley and oregano, as desired.

Serves 4 complete meals / 8-10 as side servings.

Grape Tomato and Avocado Salad

Servings: 4
Proteins/Carbs/Fats: 0 / 1 / 3

Ingredients

1 pint Grape Tomatoes

1/2 cup Parsley and/or Cilantro (chopped)

2 Tbsp Extra Virgin Olive Oil

2 Tbsp Fresh Squeezed Lemon Juice

1 Small Vidalia Onion (sliced thin)

3 small or 2 large Avocados (chopped)

To taste High Quality Sea Salt

Directions

In a non-reactive glass bowl toss together tomatoes, parsley, cilantro, oil, lemon juice, and onions.

Add avocados and salt and toss gently.

Chill if not serving immediately.

Serves 4

Submitted By: Dianne L. - Clinton Township, Michigan

www.BeyondDiet.com

Guacamole Salad

Servings: 6
Proteins/Carbs/Fats: 0 / 1 / 3

Ingredients

1 pint Grape Tomatoes (halves)

1 Yellow Bell Pepper (diced)

15 oz can Black Beans (drained)

1/2 cup Small Red Onion (diced)

2 Tbsp Jalapeno Pepper (minced)

1/2 tsp Lime Zest (fresh grated)

4 Avocados (chopped)

2 Limes

1/4 cup Olive Oil

1 Tbsp Sea Salt

1/2 tsp Black Pepper

1/2 tsp Garlic

1/4 tsp Cayenne Pepper

Directions

Whisk together lime juice, olive oil, salt, pepper, garlic and cayenne pepper.

Combine vegetables, beans and onions.

Pour lime juice mixture over vegetable mixture.

Toss well.

Right before serving, gently add chopped avocados.

Submitted By: Lona P. – Lexington, Tennessee

Avocado, Hearts of Palm, and Red Onion Salad

Servings: 8
Proteins/Carbs/Fats: 0 / .5 / 2

Ingredients

1 (14 oz) can Hearts of Palm (drained)

4 California Firm-ripe Avocados

1 Small Red Onion (sliced thin)

About 2 heads Boston Lettuce Leaves

Coriander Vinaigrette (see Dressings section)

*Salad pictured also uses quinoa and black beans.

Directions

Cut hearts of palm and avocado into 3/4-inch cubes and in a large bowl with a rubber spatula gently toss with onion and vinaigrette until combined well.

Line 8 salad plates with lettuce leaves and mound avocado mixture on top.

Submitted By: Alex

www.BeyondDiet.com

Early Summer Salad

Servings: 2
Proteins/Carbs/Fats: 2 / 2 / 0

Ingredients

3 strips Apple-Wood Smoked Bacon

8-10 Large Romaine Lettuce Leaves

1 Pear

1/2 Large Avocado

1/4 cup Dried Cherries or Cranberries

1/2 oz Sunflower Seeds

2 Tbsp Your Favorite Vinaigrette

To taste Salt and Pepper

Directions

Cook bacon, and cool on paper towel.

Wash and dry lettuce.

Slice up pear and avocado.

Roughly chop cherries and cooled bacon.

Combine all ingredients and toss with vinaigrette.

Makes two servings.

Submitted By: Danielle H. – Dallas, Texas

Bean Salads

Two Bean and Rice Salad

Servings: 16
Proteins/Carbs/Fats: 0 / 1 / 0

Ingredients

3 cups Cold Cooked Brown Rice

1 (15 oz) can Pinto Beans (rinsed and drained)

1 (15 oz) can Black Beans (rinsed and drained)

1 (10 oz) package Frozen Peas (thawed)

1 cup Celery (sliced)

1 Medium Red Onion (chopped, 1/2 cup)

2 (4 oz) cans Diced Green Chili Peppers

1/4 cup Snipped Cilantro or Parsley

Garlic Dressing (see Dressings section)

Directions

In a 2 1/2 quart covered container combine cooked rice, pinto beans, black beans, peas, celery, onion, diced green chili peppers and cilantro or parsley.

Add the dressing, and toss gently to mix. Cover and chill for up to 24 hours.

This is a great recipe for parties – it makes 16 servings.

Submitted By: Jackie G.

Italian White Bean and Artichoke Salad

Servings: 8
Proteins/Carbs/Fats: 0 / 2 / 1.5

Ingredients

6 cups Organic Spinach (thinly sliced)

2 cups Organic Red Peppers Strips

1/2 cup Organic Celery (sliced)

1/2 cup Onion (thinly sliced)

19 oz can White Beans (drained and rinsed)

14 oz can Quartered Artichoke Hearts (drained)

To taste Fresh Chopped Basil

Dressing:

5 Tbsp High Quality Organic Red Wine Vinegar

4 Tbsp Organic Extra Virgin Olive Oil

1 tsp Organic Tomato Paste

1 dash Salt

1 dash Tabasco Sauce

1-2 cloves Garlic (finely minced)

Directions

Arrange the salad ingredients for presentation and refrigerate until ready to serve. Drizzle with dressing, and toss.

To make dressing, put all ingredients in a jar and shake well. (This will make enough dressing to have leftover.)

This is a great salad to serve for guests.

Submitted By: Christine K. M. - Greeley, Colorado

Chickpea Salad

Servings: 4
Proteins/Carbs/Fats: 0 / 2 / 0

Ingredients

1 can Chickpeas (drained and rinsed)

1 cup Edamame (cooked)

1 Small Cucumber (diced)

1/2 Red Pepper (diced)

1/2 Small Red Onion (diced)

1 clove Garlic (minced)

Slivered Raw Almonds (optional)

Chives (optional)

Feta Cheese (optional)

Olive Oil

Balsamic Vinegar

Directions

Toss chickpeas, edamame, and vegetables.

Add almonds and feta cheese.

Use olive oil and balsamic vinegar for dressing.

Submitted By: Julie

Fennel, Pepper, and Garbanzo Bean Salad

Servings: 3
Proteins/Carbs/Fats: 0 / 2 / 3

Ingredients

1 Red Onion (diced)

1-2 Raw Fennel (sliced into rounds, remove leafy tops)

1-2 Red Peppers (sliced into rounds, seeds removed)

1-2 cups Garbanzo Beans

Chopped Cilantro and Parsley

1 tsp Salt

1/2 tsp Black Pepper

1/4 cup Olive Oil (scant)

1 Lemon (juiced)

Directions

Mix all ingredients together in a glass, clay bowl.

Refrigerate before serving. The taste improves when chilled overnight - if it lasts that long.

Makes 2-3 servings.

Submitted By: Naomi N. – Jerusalem, Israel

Black Bean and Cottage Cheese Salad

Ingredients

Red Leaf Lettuce

Green Leaf Lettuce

Romaine Lettuce

Cucumbers (sliced and scored)

Yellow Peppers

Green Peppers

Celery

Roma Tomatoes

Chives

1/2 cup Black Beans

1/2 cup Cottage Cheese (sprinkled with cinnamon)

To taste Sea Salt and Pepper

1 tsp Dijon Mustard

2 Tbsp + 1 tsp Red Wine Vinegar

1/2 cup Olive Oil

Directions

Combine vegetables, beans, and cottage cheese. (See picture for an aesthetically pleasing way of arranging the ingredients!)

Drizzle with a mixture of Dijon mustard, red wine vinegar, and olive oil.

Submitted By: Christina L.

Green Bean Salad with Mint

Servings: 6
Proteins/Carbs/Fats: 2 / 1 / 3

Ingredients

1 1/2 lbs Fresh Green Beans

3/4 cups Extra Virgin Olive Oil

1/2 cup Fresh Mint Leaves

1/4 cup White Wine Vinegar

1/2 tsp Salt

1 clove Garlic

1/4 tsp Freshly Ground Black Pepper

1 cup Toasted Walnuts*

1 cup Red Onion (chopped)

1 cup Crumbled Feta Cheese

Directions

Wash beans and trim ends; cut into halves or thirds. Parboil by dropping into boiling water 13 minutes. Drain and plunge into ice water 5 minutes; drain and chill.

Combine oil, mint leaves, vinegar, salt, garlic and pepper in food processor or blender and process 20 seconds; set aside. Place beans in large glass bowl and toss with toasted walnuts, red onion and feta. Pour dressing over salad and toss before serving. Best if made 2 hours ahead of time or the day before to develop flavors.

Makes 6 to 8 servings.

Note: Place walnuts on cookie sheet or in shallow pan and broil in oven until browned and aromatic, 5 minutes, stirring and turning once or twice.

Submitted By: Michael T. - Katy, Texas

Chickpea Salad

Servings: 4
Proteins/Carbs/Fats: 1 / 2 / 2

Ingredients

1 cup Quinoa

2 cups Water

2 Tbsp Honey

1/4 cup Lemon Juice

1/2 tsp Kosher Salt

3 Tbsp Olive Oil

1 cup Tart Apple (peeled and diced)

1 cup Celery (finely chopped)

1/3 cup Raisins

1/3 cup Parsley (chopped)

1/2 cup Almonds (coarsely chopped)

Directions

Rinse quinoa and bring to a boil. Turn heat down and simmer for about 15 minutes, until water is absorbed. Fluff with fork and allow to cool.

In a small bowl mix honey, lemon juice, and salt. Add oil slowly.

Add all other ingredients and mix.

Enjoy!

Chop-Chop Salad

Servings: 1
Proteins/Carbs/Fats: 0 / 3 / 2

Ingredients

1 bunch Celery

1 cup Red Kidney Beans

To Taste Salt and Fresh Ground Pepper

3 tsp Flaxseed Oil

Raw Apple Cider Vinegar

Directions

Ready in 60 seconds. It's refreshing, satisfies your taste buds, and a little Jazzy!!!

Combine ingredients and toss.

May want to add some spices – cayenne pepper, garlic, lemon pepper spice, white vinegar, etc.

Submitted By: Larisa E.

Red, White and Black Bean Salad

Servings: 6
Proteins/Carbs/Fats: 1 / 3 / 3

Ingredients

1 (15 oz) can Red Kidney Beans (rinsed and drained)

1 (15 oz) can Black Beans (rinsed and drained)

1 (15 oz) can White Beans (rinsed and drained)

1 (15 oz) can Non-GMO Sweet Corn (drained)

1/2 cup Olive Oil (or other oil)

1/4 cup Rice Vinegar or Apple Cider Vinegar

1/2 tsp Garlic Powder

1/2 tsp Ground Cumin

1/2 tsp Black Pepper

1/4 tsp Chili Powder

1/4 tsp Cayenne Pepper

Directions

Combine beans and corn in a medium- to large-sized mixing bowl.

Combine oil, vinegar and spices in a bowl. Whisk in bowl until ingredients are well mixed. Pour the entire contents of the bowl over the bean mixture. Toss to coat and to blend the colors.

This can be served immediately or made ahead and left to marinate in the refrigerator for up to 8 hours.

Submitted By: Dianne

Broccoli Salads

Broccoli Cauliflower Toss

Servings: 1
Proteins/Carbs/Fats: 3 / 3 / 0

Ingredients

1 1/2 cups Fresh Broccoli Florets

1/2 cup Fresh Cauliflowerets

1/2 cup Carrots (sliced)

1 cup Cooked Chicken (cubed)

6 Cherry Tomatoes (halved)

Red Wine Vinegar & Honey Dressing (see Dressings section)

Directions

Toss together vegetables and chicken.

Pour dressing over salad.

Cover and chill for at least 4 hours, stirring occasionally. Drain before serving.

Option: Can steam broccoli, cauliflower and carrots for 2-3 minutes if prefer less crunch. Also, this salad is tasty without the honey if avoiding sugar.

Submitted By: Grace – Springboro, Ohio

Broccoli Salad

Servings: 18
Proteins/Carbs/Fats: 0 / 1 / 2

Ingredients

2 Large Bunches Fresh Broccoli (cut into tiny florets & stalks)

2 cups Isabel's Homemade Mayonnaise (see Dressings section)

To Taste Stevia (approximately 1/8 tsp)

1/2 cup Vinegar

1/2 tsp Salt

3/4 tsp Freshly Ground Pepper

12 oz Dried Cranberries

6 oz Dried Apricots

8 oz Raw Organic Cheese (shredded)

4 oz Slivered Almonds

1 Purple Onion (diced)

Directions

Combine mayonnaise, vinegar salt and pepper, and pour over florets.

Shred stalks (1-inch pieces) and apricots together in food processor until finely chopped.

Blend all items together. Add stevia.

Best chilled after a few hours. Holds well in the fridge for a couple days.

Makes 18 servings.

Submitted By: Elise – Houston, Texas

Fresh Broccoli Salad with Raisins

Servings: 5
Proteins/Carbs/Fats: 0 / 2 / 0

Ingredients

4-5 bunches Fresh Broccoli

1 Red Onion (chopped)

1 cup White Raisins

1 cup Cashews, Walnuts, or Pecans

1 Tbsp Isabel's Homemade Mayonnaise (see Dressings section)

1 Lemon (juiced)

To taste Stevia

Directions

Chop broccoli to small flowers.

Chop onion.

Chop nuts.

Combine broccoli, onion, and nuts. Add raisins.

Combine mayonnaise, lemon juice, and stevia. Drizzle mixture over salad.

Submitted By: Ravit Elkis J. – Herzeliya, Israel

Broccoli and Pea Salad

Servings: 4
Proteins/Carbs/Fats: .5 / 2 / 2

Ingredients

2 cups Broccoli (cut into bite-sized pieces)

2 cups Sweet Peas (frozen or fresh)

1 cup Cauliflower (cut into bite-sized pieces, optional)

2 stalks Celery (sliced thin)

1/4 cup Sliced Almonds (can be roasted)

1 tsp Dried Dill

1/2 - 1 cup Isabel's Homemade Mayonnaise (see Dressings section)

Directions

Toss all vegetables together. Stir in almonds.

Add dill and mayonnaise, and mix thoroughly.

Serve chilled or at room temperature.

Submitted By: Diane – New Smyrna Beach, Florida

Broccoli-Tomato Salad

Servings: 6
Proteins/Carbs/Fats: 0 / 1 / 2

Ingredients

1 large or 2 medium Red or Purple Onions

2 cups Fresh Broccoli

2 cups Tomato (chopped)

3-4 oz Feta Cheese

3 Tbsp Olive Oil

3 Tbsp Apple Cider Vinegar

1 large or 2 small cloves Garlic (crushed)

1 tsp Mustard

To taste Salt and Pepper

Directions

The key to this salad is marinating the onions: Combine the olive oil, vinegar, garlic and mustard (with salt and pepper to taste) first thing in the morning. Slice the onions very thin, and toss them with the oil-vinegar mix. Place in the refrigerator all day.

Right before serving, toss in the other ingredients. Enjoy!

Submitted By: Cindy W. – Freiburg, Germany

Nutty Broccoli Slaw

Servings: 6
Proteins/Carbs/Fats: 0 / 1 / 2

Ingredients

2 Chicken Breasts (optional)
1/2 cup Real Bacon Bits (optional)
2 cups Cabbage
2 Carrots
1 cup Onion Greens (sliced, about 1 bunch)
2-3 cups Broccoli Florets
1 can Ripe Olives (optional)
1 cup Sunflower Seeds
3/4 cup Slivered Almonds

Directions

Cook the chicken breasts in olive oil. Let cool, then slice into thin slivers (around three inches long).

Thinly slice the cabbage and carrots.

Drain the can of olives. Cut the olives in half.

Choose a dressing of your liking (see Dressings section).

Toss all ingredients, and enjoy!

Submitted By: Olive F.

Salads With Fruit

Curried Banana Salad

Servings: 3
Proteins/Carbs/Fats: 0 / 2 / 0

Ingredients

2 Large Firm Bananas
1 Green Apple (skinned)
2 Tbsp Lemon Juice
1/2 cup Plain Yogurt
1/2 cup Sultanas
1 tsp Ground Cumin
1 dash Cayenne Pepper
1/2 tsp Salt
2 Tbsp Toasted Coconut

Directions

Peel bananas and slice in 1/2-inch rounds. Core and dice apple. Combine bananas, apple, and lemon juice.

Mix yogurt with sultanas, ground cumin, cayenne pepper and salt. Pour over banana mix and stir carefully.

Sprinkle coconut over salad at time of serving.

Submitted By: Edna P.

Green Apple Salad

Servings: 4
Proteins/Carbs/Fats: 0 / 2 / 0

Ingredients

2/3 cup Organic Yogurt (drained)

1 Tbsp Honey

1 Tbsp Grated Horseradish

2 cups Savoy Cabbage (chopped)

1 1/3 cups Green Apples (cored and sliced)

Directions

Whisk yogurt, honey and horseradish together. Add the finely chopped Savoy cabbage and sliced apples.

Chill for 1 hour before serving.

Makes 4 servings.

Submitted By: Agatha - Bermuda

Banana Delight Salad

Servings: 2
Proteins/Carbs/Fats: 0 / 2 / 0

Ingredients

1 Banana
1 Tbsp Honey
1/6 Lemon
1/2 cup Raspberries
1 1/2 Tbsp Flaxseed (ground)

Directions

Slice banana and sprinkle with juice of lemon.

Add ground flaxseed and toss lightly.

Add the raspberries, and drizzle the honey over everything.

Serves 1 or 2, or add more fruit for a full salad.

Can use any other fruit – especially good with fresh pineapple or peaches replacing the raspberries.

Submitted By: Nancy

Berry Salad

Ingredients

Mixed Lettuces

Some Spinach Leaves

Purple Onion (in thin slices)

Strawberries (sliced)

Other Berries

Goat Cheese (optional)

Nuts (coarsely chopped)

Dressing:

1 cup Olive Oil

2 Tbsp Lime Juice

1/4 cup Balsamic Vinaigrette

1/4 cup Wine

1/3 cup Berries

To taste Salt and Pepper

Directions

Toss salad ingredients together.

For the dressing, blend all the ingredients and pour over salad when ready to serve!

Submitted By: Debbie A. – Mexico City

Strawberry Balsamic Avocado Salad

Servings: 1
Proteins/Carbs/Fats: 0 / 1 / 2

Ingredients

1 handful Baby Spinach or Frisée

1/4 Avocado

2-3 Strawberries

1/4 Onion

1 Tbsp Balsamic Vinegar

1 Tbsp Coconut Oil

Walnuts (optional)

Fresh Cracked Black Pepper

*all amounts are per person

Directions

Pre-heat sauté pan to medium high with a dollop of coconut oil or butter. Slice the onion thinly and place in the pan. Cook for 1-2 minutes before tossing them so they get a little caramelized. Toss and cook for another 2 minutes. Turn down the heat to low and let sit for 10-15 minutes or whatever you have patience for. The longer the more sugary sweet they get.

Wash lettuce and set aside.

Mix the vinegar and oil together and set aside. I reduce down my balsamic to make it sweeter and burn off the alcohol taste. Bring to a slight simmer and reduce to low heat for 5 minutes.

Place lettuce on a plate or bowl and add chopped avocado, strawberries and even a couple of walnuts if you want a crunch. Top it off with the caramelized onions and drizzle the dressing over the top. Finish with fresh cracked black pepper. Enjoy.

Submitted By: Jennipher H. – Vancouver, Washington

www.BeyondDiet.com

Pear Salad

Servings: 2
Proteins/Carbs/Fats: 3 / 1 / 1

Ingredients

1 Small Head Romaine Lettuce, or Hearts of Romaine

1 Large D'Anjou Pear (cubed)

1 Red Onion (thinly sliced)

1/2-1 cup Pecans (chopped)

1/4 cup Crumbled Feta Cheese or Bleu Cheese

Pear Dressing (see Dressings section), or a Raspberry or Red Wine Vinaigrette

Directions

Toss lettuce, pear, and onion. Top with pecans and cheese. Pour dressing over all.

For dressing, combine ingredients. Mix well or shake in a jar until well blended.

Add cooked chicken to make it a full meal dish.

For another delicious take on this salad, substitute an apple for the pear.

Submitted By: Joan R.

Fresh Fruit and Nut Salad

Ingredients

Grapes

Strawberries

Kiwi

Lettuce

Baby Spinach Leaves

Chopped Pecans or Almonds

Poppy Seed Dressing

Directions

Cut up strawberries, kiwi, grapes and any other fruit you may have in your house.

Top mixture of shredded lettuce and baby spinach leaves with fruit. Add chopped pecans or almonds. Toss with a little poppy seed dressing.

Serve with salmon or broiled chicken, and enjoy!

Submitted By: Dolores

Cucumber Mango Salad

Servings: 2
Proteins/Carbs/Fats: 0 / 2 / 0

Ingredients

4 Green Onions

1 Mango (peeled, sliced, and/or chopped)

1 Small English Cucumber (sliced and/or chopped)

1 Jalapeno Pepper (seeded and sliced, optional)

To taste Stevia

2 tsp Five Spice Powder

To taste Sea Salt

Directions

Combine brown sugar, spices, and a little sea salt.

Slice green portion of green onion into thin strips; chop the white portion.

Combine green onion, mango, cucumber, jalapeno pepper, and remainder of sugar/spice mixture.

Bacon, Rice, and Mango Salad

Servings: 4
Proteins/Carbs/Fats: 1 / 3 / 2

Ingredients

Mixed Salad Greens

2 Avocados (diced)

1/2 Lemon (juiced)

3 cups Cooked Long Grain Brown Rice

4 pieces Bacon (cooked and chopped)

1 cup Bean Sprouts

1 (15 oz) can Mango Slices (drained) or use Fresh Mango (sliced or chopped)

1 Onion (thinly sliced or chopped)

1 cup Punnet Cherry Tomatoes

Basil Leaves

Vinegar, Olive Oil, and Herbs Dressing (see Dressings section)

Directions

Combine avocados with lemon juice.

Combine rice, bacon, bean sprouts, mango, onion, and tomatoes. Add avocados.

Serve over mixed salad greens and sprinkle basil leaves on top.

Drizzle dressing over.

Submitted By: Barbara H. – Adelaide, Australia

Fresh Fruit Spinach Salad with Seasoned Ground Turkey

Servings: 3
Proteins/Carbs/Fats: 2 / 1 / 2

Ingredients

Seasoned Ground Turkey:

4 oz Ground Turkey

2 Tbsp Onion (finely chopped)

2 Tbsp Red Pepper (finely chopped)

1 tsp Butter

To taste Sea Salt and Freshly Ground Black Pepper

Spinach Salad:

1 cup Fresh Spinach Leaves (stems removed)

1/4 Tomato (chopped)

1 Small Red Apple (1/2 finely chopped, 1/2 sliced)

2 oz Avocado

1 oz Raw Almonds (finely chopped)

2 tsp Extra Virgin Olive Oil

1 Lemon (squeezed)

1 Strawberry (sliced)

Directions

In a skillet, warm the butter. Add the ground turkey, onion, and red pepper and cook over medium heat. Add sea salt and ground black pepper for taste. Stir occasionally until crisp, and then remove the skillet from the heat.

For the salad, in a medium salad bowl, toss together the spinach and tomato, then gently mix in the extra virgin olive oil and lemon juice. Transfer to a serving bowl. Top with the seasoned ground turkey, finely chopped apple and raw almonds. Garnish with side of avocado (lightly peppered), apple slices, and strawberry in center. Serve warm.

Submitted By: Julie M. - Webster, Texas

Salads with Meat

New York Strip Steak and Romaine Salad

Servings: 3
Proteins/Carbs/Fats: 4 / 1 / 1

Ingredients

12 oz New York Strip Steak

1 head Romaine Lettuce

1 Red Onion

2 Green Bell Peppers (red, yellow, or orange can be substituted)

1 Small Block of Blue Cheese (crumbled)

Italian Dressing

Directions

After cooking New York strip steak, slice it into thin pieces.

Chop Romaine lettuce.

Slice red onion and peppers.

Combine all ingredients, and drizzle with Italian dressing. Enjoy!

Submitted By: Anthony S.

Gloria's Cool, Crisp, Yummy Salad

Servings: 6
Proteins/Carbs/Fats: 0 / 1 / 3

Ingredients

3 heads Romaine Lettuce

1 Large Sweet Onion

1-2 Avocados

Pecorino Cheese

1-2 Lemons (squeezed for juice)

1/4 cup Olive Oil

To taste Salt and Pepper

Grilled Steak or Chicken

*Ingredients are designed for making large protions. Adjust as needed.

Directions

Wash Romaine lettuce. Cut into large slices and break up a bit (keep pieces on the large size for the crunch).

Cut onions into 1/4-inch rings and then slice rings into thirds.

Slice avocados and arrange over lettuce.

Slice meat into bite-sized pieces and add to salad.

Combine lemon juice and olive oil, and pour over salad.

Grate Pecorino cheese over salad.

Enjoy!

This salad is still yummy after a day – a bit softer, but still very tasty.

Mincemeat Salad

Servings: 4
Proteins/Carbs/Fats: 2 / 1 / 0

Ingredients

1 tsp Butter

2-2 1/2 cups Mince (can use any, but beef is tasty)

2 cloves Garlic (minced)

2 cups Vegetables (diced small, whatever you have in the fridge is good)

1/2 cup Beef Stock

1 dash Soy Sauce

To taste Salt and Pepper

Mixed Salad Leaves

Cherry Tomatoes

1/2 Pepper (diced)

Any other salad ingredients that you have and enjoy

Directions

Heat the butter and brown the mince.

Add garlic, cook until fragrant.

Add diced vegetables and cook for 2 minutes.

Add stock, soy sauce, and season to taste.

Bring to a boil and then lower heat and simmer until meat and vegetables are cooked and stock has reduced and thickened slightly.

Meanwhile, plate salad ingredients. When meat is cooked spoon some over your salad. Serve immediately.

Submitted By: Kate C. – Binghamton, New York

Club Sandwich Salad

Servings: 4
Proteins/Carbs/Fats: 4 / 1 / 2

Ingredients

1 Small Head of Green Leaf Lettuce

1 Small Head of Red Leaf Lettuce

1 cup Cherry Tomatoes or Small Salad Tomatoes

1 Large Ripe Avocado, or 2 Small Ones

1/2 lb Nitrate-Free Bacon

1/2 lb Nitrate-Free Roast Turkey (can use deli-sliced, but not shaved)

2-3 oz Organic Sharp Cheddar Cheese (or Swiss or Parmesan Cheese if you prefer)

4 slices Spelt or Rice Bread

1 Large Clove Garlic

1-2 Tbsp Organic Butter

Directions

Fry bacon until crumbly, drain and set aside to cool.

Slice turkey into 1/2-inch cubes, or tear deli-sliced turkey into pieces.

Use a vegetable peeler to slice cheese thinly.

Wash lettuce and tear into bite-sized pieces.

Slice cherry tomatoes in half or if using salad tomatoes, halve and slice about 1/4-inch thick.

Peel and slice avocados lengthwise.

Toast bread, rub with cut side of garlic clove and then butter toast. Cut each toast slice into 8 triangles.

In large bowl, toss lettuce and dressing to coat well.

Submitted By: Mary B. – Phoenix, Arizona

Layered BLT Salad

Servings: 4
Proteins/Carbs/Fats: 1 / 1 / 2

Ingredients

1 head Butter Leaf Lettuce

1 Cucumber (sliced)

1/2 cup Isabel's Homemade Mayonnaise (see Dressings section)

To taste Organic Parmesan

4-5 slices Turkey Bacon (crumbled)

3 Small Tomatoes (grilled or oven roasted)

Directions

Layer 1/3 of each of the ingredients in the order listed. Repeat to make 3 complete layers.

Submitted By: Tommy and Patty L. – Smyrna, Tennessee

Pea Salad with Bacon

Servings: 4
Proteins/Carbs/Fats: 1 / 2 / 0

Ingredients

1 bag Frozen Peas or 2-3 cups Fresh Peas

3 stalks Celery (chopped)

1 Small Red Onion (finely chopped)

3-5 strips Bacon

Isabel's Homemade Mayonnaise (see Dressings section) or Plain Yogurt

Directions

Thaw peas.

Chop the onion and celery and toss together with the peas. Add in the mayo or yogurt until you get it to the desired consistency.

Fry the bacon crispy and top each portion of salad with a sprinkling of bacon.

Variation: Add 1 cup cooked and cooled tri-colored quinoa to salad, increasing the amount of mayo till desired consistency is met. Can also add some chopped red pepper to add some color!

Submitted By: Claudia B.

Salads with Nuts

Salad with Chia Seeds and Crushed Walnuts

Servings: 2
Proteins/Carbs/Fats: 2 / 1 / 0

Ingredients

1 1/2 head Red Leaf Lettuce

1 heart Romaine Lettuce

1/2 cup Red Bell Peppers (diced)

1/2 cup Carrots (diced)

1/2 cup Walnuts (coarsely chopped)

1/2 cup Chia Seeds

Small Portion of Parmesan Cheese Shavings

Directions

Tear lettuce into smaller pieces and toss.

Arrange ingredients, in order listed, divided onto four salad plates and drizzle with basic vinaigrette recipe (see Dressing section).

Submitted By: W.R. Bates – Indianapolis, Indiana

Sue's Waldorf Salad for One

Servings: 1
Proteins/Carbs/Fats: 2 / 2 / 0

Ingredients

1 cup Celery
1 Small Apple (any type)
1/4 cup Walnuts (chopped)
1 Lime
Small Cubes of Cheese
(optional)

Directions

Wash and chop celery.

Wash, core, and chop apple.

Combine celery, apple, and walnuts.

Squeeze juice from the lime over the mixture.

Add cheese cubes, if desired.

Submitted By: Sue M.

Beetroot Salad

Ingredients

Whole Beetroot

Arugula

Walnuts

Feta Cheese

Red Onion

Balsamic Vinegar

Directions

Roast whole beetroot in medium oven for an hour, or until soft in center. Cool and cube (with or without skins).

Chop the walnuts. Chop the feta cheese. Finely slice the onion.

Place beetroot, arugula, walnuts, feta cheese and onion in a salad bowl.

Drizzle with balsamic vinegar. If that is too bitter, try White Balsamic & Dijon Mustard Vinaigrette or Mustard Vinaigrette (see Dressings section).

Submitted By: Edwina G. – Adelaide, Australia

Baby Arugula and Walnut Salad

Ingredients

1 bunch Fresh Baby Arugula

Red Onions (thinly sliced)

Parmesan Cheese (shaved or shredded)

Garlic Powder

Celtic Sea Salt

Black Pepper

Raw Walnut Pieces

1/2 cup Extra Virgin Olive Oil

1/4 cup White Balsamic Vinegar

Directions

Toss together arugula and onions.

Add walnut pieces, garlic powder, salt and pepper.

Add olive oil and balsamic vinegar.

Toss again, and enjoy!

Submitted By: Caroline G.– Venetia, Pennsylvania

Carrot Ribbons with Cashews

Servings: 8
Proteins/Carbs/Fats: 1 / 1 / 1

Ingredients

1 1/2 lb Carrots

1/2 cup Whole Cashews

3 Tbsp Butter

3/4 cup Yellow Onion (finely chopped)

2 tsp Fresh Ginger (minced)

To taste Stevia

1/2 tsp Salt

1/8 tsp Cinnamon + 1 stick

Directions

Cut the carrots into ribbons using a peeler down the length of the carrot.

Cook the onion, ginger, and salt in the butter, stirring occasionally, until the onions are translucent (about 10 minutes).

Add the carrots, remaining spices, and 1 tablespoon water. Cook, covered, for 5 minutes.

Remove whole spices, toss in the cashews, and serve hot (the leftovers are excellent cold).

Makes 8 servings.

Spinach Salads

Spinach and Chicken Salad

Servings: 4
Proteins/Carbs/Fats: 1 / 1 / 0

Ingredients

8-10 Spinach Leaves

6 Medium White Mushrooms

1 Chicken Breast

6 Raw Almonds

1 Lemon

Dashes Red Wine Vinegar

To taste Sea Salt and Fresh Ground Pepper

To taste Garlic Salt (without sugar)

Directions

Wash and dry spinach. Lay spinach on plate to make a spinach bed.

Sauté mushrooms in small amount of butter, sea salt, and red wine vinegar pour over spinach.

Heat chicken in pan with dash of red wine vinegar and garlic salt. Put chicken on top of mushrooms, cut up tomato and place on chicken.

Grate the almonds over the top of whole salad. Squeeze the lemon juice out of one lemon over the top of whole salad; add some more sea salt and fresh ground pepper.

Submitted By: Kara F. – Troutdale, Oregon

www.BeyondDiet.com

Popeye the Sailor Quiche

Servings: 4
Proteins/Carbs/Fats: 2 / 1 / .5

Ingredients

1 cup Fresh Baby Organic
Spinach Leaves

1/4 Onion

2 tsp Olive Oil

1 (6-10") Zucchini

3-4 slices Turkey Pastrami

4 Large Eggs

To Taste Granulated Garlic or
Fresh Crushed Garlic

To taste Sea Salt and Coarse
Ground Black Pepper

1 cup Cooked Brown Rice
(optional)

Directions

Heat a deep 10" skillet,
spreading the olive oil around.

Slice ¼ of the onion and cut
into quarters and add to pan.
Slice zucchini into 1/8" slices
and add to pan. Tear small
pieces of pastrami and add to
pan. Stir a little and brown
zucchini while adding the
spinach and stir until it gets
wilted.

Add cooked brown rice if a
larger portion is needed.

Lightly beat eggs and add to
pan. Stir for a few seconds to
get the egg on everything. Let
cook for a minute or two until
bottom is brown. Separate
into quarters and flip over to
brown other side. Add Pepper
Jack cheese on top while hot
so cheese melts all over. (Skip
cheese if want to watch fat.)
Sprinkle with sea salt, garlic,
and pepper.

Submitted By: Brian

Parmesan Spinach Salad

Servings: 4
Proteins/Carbs/Fats: 1 / 2 / 1

Ingredients

1 bag Baby Organic Spinach Leaves (torn into pieces)

15-20 Organic Grape Tomatoes (cut in half)

1/2 jar Roasted Red Pepper (sliced)

1 Orange (sectioned and skin removed) or 1 large can Mandarin Oranges (drained)

1/2 cup Almond Slivers or Pine Nuts

1 Avocado (cut into slices)

Shavings of Parmesan Cheese as a Garnish

Citrus Vinaigrette (see Dressings section)

Directions

Arrange ingredients, in the order listed, dividing between four salad plates.

Drizzle with citrus vinaigrette, and enjoy!

Submitted By: E.M. Edson

Lona's Healthy Spinach Salad

Servings: 2
Proteins/Carbs/Fats: 3 / 4 / 1

Ingredients

8 Large Eggs (hard boiled, 6 yolks discarded)

6 cups Baby Spinach

4 Tbsp Low Fat Creamy Blue Cheese Dressing (see Dressings section, divided)

8 oz can Sliced Beets (rinsed)

1 cup Carrots (shredded)

2 Tbsp Pecans (chopped)

Directions

Peel the boiled eggs and discard 6 of the yolks. Chop the remaining yolks and whites.

Toss spinach and 2 tablespoons of the homemade dressing in a large bowl.

Divide between 2 plates and top with chopped eggs, beets, carrots and pecans.

Drizzle each with 1 tablespoon of the remaining dressing.

Submitted By: Lona P. – Lexington, Tennessee

Veggie Salad

Servings: 8
Proteins/Carbs/Fats: 0 / 2 / 0

Ingredients

8 cups Fresh Spinach
2 Red Bell Peppers
5 Medium Carrots
1 Large European Cucumber
30 Cherry Tomatoes
1 Red Onion

Directions

Wash spinach and remove stems, tear in bite-size pieces.

Clean inside or bell peppers and cut in bite-sized pieces.

Peel carrots and slice fairly thinly, cut slices in half if too large.

Peel cucumber and cut in four, lengthwise, and then in 1/2-inch thick slices.

Cut cherry tomatoes in half.

Remove outside layer of onion and cut ends off then chop finely.

Assemble ingredients in a large bowl and mix.

Serve with a dash of olive oil, salt and pepper.

Submitted By: Sonia W. – Grez-sur-Loing, France

www.BeyondDiet.com

Eagle Salad

Ingredients

Spinach

Tomatoes

Onions

Celery

Mushrooms

Peppers

Strawberries

Pineapple

Blueberries

1-2 Tbsp Hemp Hearts

2 Tsbp Extra Virgin Olive Oil

1 Tbsp Apple Cider Vinegar

1 tsp Lemon Juice

Directions

Cut up spinach and spread over plate.

Cut up all vegetables and fruit. Spread over spinach.

Drizzle mix of olive oil, vinegar, and lemon juice over everything.

Add hemp hearts.

Submitted By: Brenda E.

Spinach and Avocado Salad

Servings: 8
Proteins/Carbs/Fats: 0 / .5 / 2

Ingredients

30 (90g/3oz) English Spinach Leaves

1 Red or Green Curly-Leafed Lettuce (or any combination)

2 Medium Avocados

3 Tbsp Extra Virgin Olive Oil

2 tsp Sesame Seeds

1 Tbsp Lemon Juice

2 tsp Wholegrain Mustard

Directions

Wash and thoroughly dry the spinach and lettuce leaves. Tear leaves into bite-sized pieces, and place in a large serving bowl.

Peel the avocados and cut into thin slices. Scatter over the leaves.

Heat 1 tablespoon of oil in a small pan. Add the sesame seeds and cook over low heat until they just start to turn golden. Remove from the heat immediately and allow to cool slightly.

Add the lemon juice, remaining oil and mustard to the pan. Stir to combine.

While still warm, pour over the salad and toss gently to coat leaves. Salad is best served immediately.

Makes 8 servings.

Submitted By: Kerry B. – Karoonda, South Australia

www.BeyondDiet.com

Eagle Salad

Servings: 4
Proteins/Carbs/Fats: 0 / 2 / 3

Ingredients

1 bunch (250 g) Washed Baby Spinach

1/4 cup Olive Oil (first harvest, cold pressed extra virgin if possilbe – this is a lovely fruity flavored oil)

6-8 Sun Dried Tomatoes (in olive oil)

1 Red Onion (halved and sliced finely)

1/4 cup Good Quality Balsamic Vinegar (white or red)

2 Firm Ripe Truss Tomatoes (quartered and sliced)

Directions

Place spinach in shallow serving dish.

In a small dish, place balsamic vinegar and sliced onions. Let stand for 10 - 15 minutes – this helps reduce strong onion taste.

Prepare sun dried tomatoes. Halve length ways, and slice in 1/8-inch slices. Add to vinegar in small bowl. Add quartered sliced fresh tomatoes and virgin olive oil. Mix all ingredients and pour over spinach, just enough to coat leaves.

Toss, mixing well, and adding dressing as necessary.

Seasoning optional.

Pink salt flakes and freshly ground pepper may be added just before serving.

Submitted By: Esther - Australia

Salad Dressings

Garlic Dressing

- **1/3 cup** White Wine Vinegar
- **1/4 cup** Olive Oil
- **2 Tbsp** Water
- **3/4 tsp** Salt
- **1/2 tsp** Garlic Powder
- **1/2 tsp** Pepper

Combine all ingredients in a screw-top jar. Cover and shake well to mix. Makes about 2/3 cup.

Submitted By: Jackie G.

Rosemary Lemon Vinaigrette

- **3/4 cup** Olive Oil
- **1/4 cup** Balsamic Vinegar
- **1 Tbsp** Citrus Juice (lemon, lime, orange, etc.)
- **1 Tbsp** Raw Honey
- **1 Tbsp** Water
- **1 tsp** Dried Rosemary, Basil, or Parsley (any herb will do!)
- **1 tsp** Pure Sea Salt
- **1 tsp** Black Pepper
- **1 tsp** Minced Garlic

Place all ingredients into a shaker and marry them ferociously or beat the vinegar and other ingredients together (except the oil) until well blended. Then, whisk in small amounts of oil until fully blended.

Submitted By: Emily P. – Saint Louis, Missouri

Basic Tasty Vinaigrette Recipe

- **1 Tbsp** Red Wine Vinegar (organic)
- **1 Tbsp** Olive Oil
- **1 Tbsp** Organic Dijon Mustard
- **1 tsp** Raw Honey (optional)
- **1/2 tsp** Coarse Sea Salt
- **1/2 tsp** Freshly Ground Black Pepper

Mix all ingredients together in a bowl.

Club Sandwich Salad Dressing

- **4 Tbsp** Isabel's Homemade Mayonnaise
- **2 Tbsp** Dijon Mustard
- **1 Tbsp** Cream
- **1 Tbsp** Yogurt
- **1 tsp** Lemon Juice (or cider vinegar)
- **1/2 tsp** Raw Honey
- **1 clove** Garlic (minced)
- **1 pinch each** Cayenne and Paprika
- **To taste** Salt and Black Pepper

Blend all ingredients well.

Submitted By: Mary B.– Phoenix, Arizona

Sun-Dried Tomato Vinaigrette

- **3/4 cup** Sherry Vinegar

- **1/2 cup** Sun-Dried Tomatoes (chopped)

- **1/2 cup** Kalamata Olives (pitted and chopped)

- **1/4 cup** Niçoise Olives (pitted and chopped)

- **1/4 cup** Honey

- **3 Tbsp** Drained Chopped Capers

- **2 Tbsp** Minced Shallot

- **2 Tbsp** Chopped Parsley Leaves

- **1 1/2 Tbsp** Chopped Mint Leaves

- **1 Tbsp** Chopped Basil Leaves

- **1 Tbsp** Minced Garlic

- **1 Tbsp** Grated Orange Zest

- **To taste** Salt and Pepper

Put all the ingredients together in a large mixing bowl, adding a little salt and pepper. With a wire whisk, whisk them together briefly, then taste and, if necessary, adjust the seasonings with more salt and pepper. Cover and refrigerate until ready to use. Makes 5 cups.

Submitted By: Angela M. – Kennedy Saskatchewan Canada

Lemon Balsamic Vinaigrette

- **1/4 cup** Lemon Juice
- **2 Tbsp** Balsamic Vinegar
- **To taste** Stevia
- **1 tsp** Salt
- **1/2 tsp** Black Pepper
- **1/2 tsp** Cumin
- **1 Tbsp** Olive Oil

Combine all ingredients. Mix or shake well.

Submitted By: Noha E.

Lemon Vinaigrette

- **1/4 cup** Freshly Squeezed Lemon Juice
- **1 cup** Olive Oil
- **1/4 tsp** Garlic (finely minced)
- **1 pinch** Sugar
- **To taste** Salt and Pepper

Drizzle oil into lemon juice and whip with a whisk to emulsify.

Submitted By: Carolyn P.

Pesto Dressing

- **1/4 cup** Olive Oil
- **1/4 cup** Red Wine Vinegar
- **3 Tbsp** Prepared Basil Pesto
- **1 clove** Garlic (minced)
- **1/4 cup** Chopped Flat Leaf Parsley
- **1/4 tsp each** Fresh Ground Sea Salt and Black Pepper

Submitted By: Terry – Cambridge, Ontario, Canada

Garlic Vinaigrette

- **3/4 cup** Olive Oil
- **1/4 cup** Cider or Red Wine Vinegar
- **2 cloves** Garlic (minced or put in a press)
- **3 tsp** of Dijon mustard
- **1 tsp** of Worcestershire Sauce
- **1/2 tsp** of salt
- **1/2 tsp** of lemon juice
- **1/4 tsp** of pepper
- **1/4 tsp** of sugar

Submitted By: Randal V.

White Balsamic & Dijon Mustard Vinaigrette

- **2 Tbsp** White Balsamic Vinegar

- **1 Tbsp** Dijon Mustard

- **6 Tbsp** Extra-Virgin Olive Oil

- **To taste** Sea Salt and Freshly Ground Pepper

In a small bowl, whisk together, vinegar and mustard. Slowly all oil in a steady stream, whisking to emulsify. Season with salt and pepper to taste. Makes about 1/4 cup.

Submitted By: Susie M.

Basic No-Fat Vinaigrette

- **3 parts** Orange Juice

- **1 part** White Balsamic Vinegar

- **2 tsp** Chopped Fresh Mixed Herbs (or 1 teaspoon dried mixed herbs)

- **1 pinch** Salt and Freshly Ground Black Pepper

Put everything into a screwtop jar and shake. You can use the dressing immediately, but it is really better to make it beforehand and then store it in the refrigerator to allow the flavours to blend.

Submitted By: Lee Faber

Mustard Vinaigrette

- **1/4 cup** Red Wine Vinegar

- **1 clove** Garlic

- **1 Tbsp** Dijon Mustard

- **1/4 tsp** Pepper (coarse or regular)

- **1/2 tsp** Honey or Stevia (to taste)

- **1/2 cup** Olive oil

- **To taste** Salt

Combine first five ingredients in a blender and turn on. Blend all ingredients. Then, with motor on, slowly drizzle the olive oil in a slow, thin stream. Makes ¾ cup and can be refrigerated for one day. Use as a dip for cold asparagus.

Submitted By: Paul M.

White Wine Marinade

- **3 Tbsp** Olive Oil
- **1 cup** Onion (finely chopped)
- **3 cloves** Garlic (finely chopped)
- **1/4 cup** Tarragon Vinegar
- **1 cup** Dry White Wine
- **1 tsp** Dried Thyme
- **1 tsp** Crushed Dried Rosemary
- **1** Bay Leaf
- **6** Black Peppercorns
- **6 sprigs** Parsley

Heat a saucepan over moderate heat. Add olive oil and heat it. Add onions and garlic. Cook about 5 minutes, stirring constantly until the onions are soft. Add vinegar and raise the heat to moderately high. Cook until the mixture is reduced by half. Add the wine, thyme, rosemary, bay leaf, parsley and peppercorns. Bring mixture to a boil, reduce heat and simmer for 5 minutes. Remove pan from heat and let marinade cool.

Submitted By: Paul M.

Citrus Vinaigrette

- **1/4 cup** Extra Virgin Olive Oil
- Juice of One Lemon
- **1 Tbsp** Fresh Orange Juice
- **1/2 tsp** Lemon Zest
- **1 tsp** Honey (optional)
- **1/2 tsp** Sea Salt
- **1/2 tsp** Freshly Ground Black Pepper

Whisk ingredients together in a medium bowl.

Submitted By: E.M. Edson

Pear Dressing

- **1/2 cup** Olive Oil
- **2-3 Tbsp** Pear Vinegar
- **1/4 cup** Honey
- **1 Dash** Salt

Submitted By: Joan R.

Easy Low-Fat Blue Cheese Dressing

- **1/3 cup** Mayonnaise (Isabel's Homemade Mayonnaise)
- **2/3 cup** Greek Yogurt
- **2 Tbsp** White Vinegar
- **1 Tbsp** Dijon Mustard
- **1/2 tsp** Salt
- **1/2 tsp** Black Pepper
- **1/4 cup (1 oz.)** Crumbled Blue Cheese

Submitted By: Lona P. – Lexington, Tennessee

Olive Oil & Lemon Juice Dressing

- **1/2 cup** Extra Virgin Olive Oil
- **1/2 cup** Lemon Juice
- **1 tsp** Dried Oregano
- **1 tsp** Salt
- **1/2 tsp** Pepper

In large bowl, whisk together oil, lemon juice, oregano, salt and pepper.

Recipe Courtesy of Canadian Living Magazine

Submitted by: Tammy K. – Calgary, Alberta, Canada

Peanut Butter Dressing

- **6 Tbsp** Raw Peanut Butter
- **2 Tbsp** Organic Soy Sauce
- **1 Tbsp** Stevia
- **1/3 cup** Olive Oil
- **1/3 cup** Filtered Water
- **1 pinch** Red Pepper Flakes

Submitted By: Susan S.

Geary's Healthy-Fat Blend Balsamic Vinaigrette Dressing

Fill your salad dressing container with these approximate ratios of liquids:

- **1/3 of container** filled with balsamic vinegar
- **1/3 of container** filled with apple cider vinegar
- **Fill the remaining 1/3 of container** with equal parts of extra virgin olive oil and "Udo's Choice EFA Oil Blend."

Add just a small touch (approximately 1 or 2 teaspoons) of real maple syrup. Add a little bit of onion powder, garlic powder, and black pepper and then shake the container to mix all ingredients well.

Submitted By Mike Geary, author of The Truth about Six Pack Abs & The Fat Burning Kitchen http://abtruth.thedsp.info

Stevia & Rice Wine Vinegar Dressing

- **2 Tbsp** Stevia
- **1 tsp** Pepper
- **1 tsp** Salt
- **1 cup** Olive Oil
- **6 tsp** Rice Wine Vinegar

Red Wine Vinegar & Honey Dressing

- **2/3 cup** Olive Oil
- **1/3 cup** Red Wine Vinegar
- **2 tsp** Honey
- **1 tsp** Minced Fresh Basil
- **1/2 tsp** Salt
- **1/4 tsp** Pepper

Whisk ingredients until well blended.

Submitted By: Grace – Springboro, Ohio

Coriander Vinaigrette

- **1** Small Garlic Clove
- **1/4 cup** Fresh Coriander
- **3 Tbsp** Fresh Lemon Juice
- **1/2 tsp** Honey
- **1/4 tsp** Salt
- **1/2 cup** Olive Oil

In a blender purée garlic and coriander with lemon juice, sugar, and salt. With motor running add oil in a stream, blending until dressing is emulsified.

Submitted By: Alex

Olive Oil & Lemon Juice Dressing

- **1/4 cup** Organic Olive Oil
- **1 tsp** Honey (or sweeten with a couple of drops of stevia)
- **1/4 cup** Lemon Juice
- **3/4 tsp** Cumin
- **1/2 tsp** Cayenne Pepper

Vinegar, Olive Oil, and Herbs

- **1/4 cup** Olive Oil
- **1 Tbsp** White Wine Vinegar
- **1 Tbsp** Red Wine Vinegar
- **1 clove** Garlic (crushed)
- **1 tsp each** Chopped Fresh Parsley and Basil
- **To taste** salt and freshly ground black pepper

Submitted By: Barbara H. – Adelaide, Australia

Fish Sauce Dressing

- **2 Tbsp** Fish Sauce (patis)
- **1 1/2 Tbsp** Fresh Lime Juice (if lime is not available, you can mix lemon and kalamansi to have the taste of lime)
- **1 Tbsp** Water
- **To taste** Stevia

Combine ingredients in a small bowl. Stir to dissolve the stevia.

Submitted By: Marife A.

Eva's Thousand Island Dressing

- **4 Tbsp** of Isabel's Homemade Mayonnaise
- **1 tsp** of dill relish
- **1 tsp** of dill pickle liquid
- **1** medium tomato, cut in half, then grated from inside (do not use skin), use all the juice and seeds.

Mix well. Add sea salt, pepper, and stevia to taste. It should be a little sweet.

Submitted By: Joan D.

Tamari Olive Oil Sauce

- **1/2 cup** Organic Tamari Soy Sauce
- **2/3 cup** Olive Oil
- **2 cloves** Garlic (crushed)
- **4 Tbsp** Lemon Juice (approximately 1 lemon)
- **2 tsp** Raw Honey, or 1 tsp Stevia

Mix ingredients together, and shake well.

Submitted By: Jeanne D. – Saint John, New Brunswick, Canada

Honey Mustard Dressing

- **1 tsp** of raw honey
- **1 tsp** of raw maple syrup
- **2 Tbsp** of olive oil
- **2 tsp** of Dijon mustard
- **2 tsp** of organic salsa
- **1 Tbsp** of apple cider vinegar
- Salt, pepper, and party spices

Submitted by: Nicolas – Trois-Rivieres, Quebec, Canada

Calico Dressing

- **1/2 cup** Stevia Blend (Steviva brand)
- **3/4 cup** White Vinegar
- **2 Tbsp** Olive Oil
- **1 Tbsp** Flaxseed Oil (after cooling, optional)

In small saucepan, combine stevia blend, white vinegar and olive oil. Bring to a boil, remove from heat, and cool. Add flaxseed oil (optional). Shake in a jar to mix.

Submitted By: Marilyn S. – Myrtle Point, Oregon

Isabel's Homemade Mayonnaise

Ingredients

- **1 cup** Olive Oil

- **1** Egg

- Juice of 1 Lemon, or Vinegar

- **1 pinch** of salt (and pepper, if desired)

- Water to thin the mayonnaise

Directions

1. Separate the eggs in your recipe. Reserve the whites for other recipes.

2. Combine the egg and lemon (or vinegar) in the bowl, whisking to mix. Continue to whisk constantly, adding the oil in a slow, steady stream. (You can make mayonnaise in a food processor or by hand, with a mixing bowl and whisk. The key for either method is to add oil very slowly, in a steady stream, while the processor is running or you're whisking vigorously.)

3. Continue to whisk constantly, adding the oil in a slow, steady stream. If the mayonnaise starts looking too thick, add enough water to thin it to the consistency you desire. Add about a teaspoon of water at a time.

4. When the oil is all mixed in, the mayonnaise should be thick and fluffy, with your whisk forming ribbons through the mixture.

5. If it never thickened and you're stirring a puddle, chances are you will need to start over. (Or, if you're still partway through the process, you can save the emulsion by adding another egg yolk, whisking vigorously. Add in remaining oil, plus extra for a double recipe.)

6. Adjust the seasoning with the salt and pepper and more lemon juice, if desired.

7. Store fresh mayonnaise in the refrigerator and use within five days.

By Isabel De Los Rios

So...just who is Isabel De Los Rios?

Isabel De Los Rios is a certified nutritionist and exercise specialist who has already helped more than 300,000 people all over the world lose incredible amounts of weight, regain their health and permanently change their lives. She is the author of The Beyond Diet Program and has become the #1 "go-to girl" when it comes to fat-burning nutrition by several of the most popular fitness professionals around the globe. Isabel's cutting-edge and completely different approach to nutrition is what sets her apart from all the rest. Her strategies work, hands down, as long as her simple principles are followed.

Isabel found her passion for nutrition as a teenager. The overweight daughter and granddaughter of type 2 diabetics, Isabel was told she was doomed to suffer from the same health problems as the generations who preceded her. Not willing to sit around waiting for this grim prediction to become a reality, she pored over every nutrition and diet book available in search of the answers to her family's weight and health problems. This led her to personally seek out doctors and health professionals that were using nutrition to get great results (as far as health and weight loss) with their patients and clients.

Isabel is able to educate clients and readers all over the world through her books, hundreds of online articles, seminars, and the media, focusing on the essential principles of fat-loss nutrition and achieving a healthy, toned, and vibrant body.

Isabel graduated from Rutgers University with a degree in exercise physiology (a pre-med curriculum). She is a Certified Strength and Conditioning Specialist, the highest and most advanced certification given by the National Strength and Conditioning Association. She is also a Holistic Nutrition Lifestyle Coach, certified by the Corrective Holistic Exercise Kinesiology (C.H.E.K.) Institute in San Diego, California. She counsels many special populations, including people with diabetes and heart disease, cancer survivors, and overweight individuals, as well as healthy individuals who wish to maintain their health and prevent disease.

She has since reached and maintained an ideal weight, is vibrantly healthy, and shows no indication that conditions like diabetes will affect her as they have so many in her family. She truly enjoys a high level of well-being that not only surprises most people, but motivates them to achieve what Isabel has.

Notes:

www.BeyondDiet.com